INSECTS

by GEORGE S. FICHTER

M.Sc., Entomology
North Carolina State College
Raleigh, North Carolina

Under the Editorship of

HERBERT S. ZIM, Ph.D.

Illustrated by

NICHOLAS STREKALOVSKY

A GOLDEN NATURE GUIDE

GOLDEN PRESS **NEW YORK**

Western Publishing Company, Inc.

FOREWORD

Despite modern technology, man still depends wholly on the products of nature for survival. Hence the battle to control insect pests is a never-ending necessity.

This book describes more than 350 pests that are found in middle North America. The illustrations, skillfully rendered by Nicholas Strekalovsky, will help identify the pest, its life stages, and the kind of damage it does. The best times and methods of control are suggested, but as these vary locally, get the advice of an entomologist or an agricultural agent before attempting major controls. The pest groupings in this book are based on where usual damage occurs. At times when they are abundant, however, pests become less selective. A field pest then, for example, may become bothersome in gardens. Insecticides are the best means to get immediate results, but remember: insecticides are poisonous. Follow directions and heed all precautions on the label.

A number of people gave advice and assistance in the preparation of this book. These included Dr. J. F. Gates Clarke and his staff at the U.S. National Museum. Also of great help were Robert H. Nelson and members of the Entomological Society of America. Dr. Jean L. Laffoon was especially helpful, as were Dr. George Anastos, Dr. R. M. Baranowski, Dr. Ralph Crabill, Dr. Richard L. Doutt, Dr. Richard C. Froeschner, Dr. Herbert W. Levi, Dr. Franklin B. Lewis, and Dr. Howard V. Weems.

G. S. F.

CONTENTS

INTRODUCTION TO INSECT PESTS

Insects exist in enormous numbers. The average insect population per square mile is estimated to be equal to the total world population of people, and in severe outbreaks a pest species far exceeds its normal numbers. In one fly infestation, experts estimated 15,000 flies per cow. Billions of hungry grasshoppers may darken the sky and devour all vegetation in their path.

Insect destruction of crops in the United States ranges from 4 billion to 15 billion dollars annually. Damage to cotton by one insect, the Boll Weevil, amounts to more than 300 million dollars a year. Termites consume about 100 million dollars' worth of wood structures, while forest insects destroy more wood than do forest fires. Insect damage cancels out the total year's efforts of about one million workers.

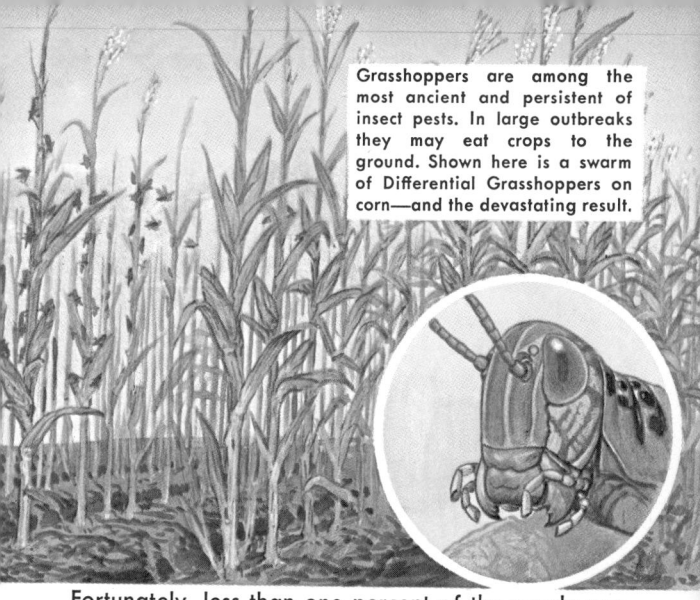

Grasshoppers are among the most ancient and persistent of insect pests. In large outbreaks they may eat crops to the ground. Shown here is a swarm of Differential Grasshoppers on corn—and the devastating result.

Fortunately, less than one percent of the nearly one million insect species are pests of man, his domestic animals, and useful plants. Of the 100,000 insect species that occur in the United States, only about 600 are considered serious pests.

Damage done by insect pests is easy to appraise. The value of beneficial species is harder to estimate. Bees, wasps, flies, butterflies, and other insects pollinate flowers that provide us with fruits and vegetables. Honey, wax, and silk are important commercial products obtained from insects. Some insect species are vital links in the food chains of fishes, birds, and other animals. Other insects are parasites or predators of damaging pests or are scavengers of animal and vegetable debris. Control measures used against harmful insects must be weighed carefully to determine the ultimate effect on all living things, including man.

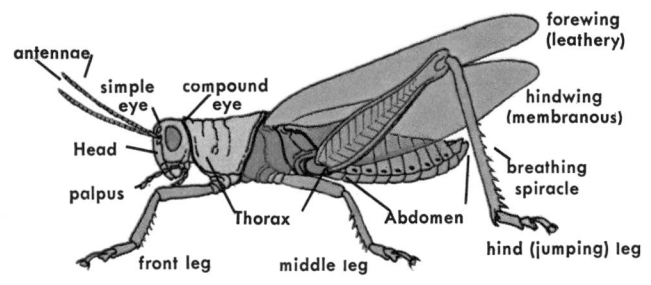

PARTS OF A TYPICAL INSECT

INSECTS AND THEIR CLOSE RELATIVES are arthropods, or "jointed-legged" animals, a large group that includes more than 85 percent of the known species of animals. About 90 percent of all the arthropods are insects. An insect's body has three distinct regions— head, thorax, and abdomen. Attached to its thorax are three pairs of legs, and in most species, two pairs of wings. Its head bears a pair of antennae. This combination of features distinguishes insects (class Insecta) from such closely related land animals as spiders, ticks, mites, centipedes, and millipedes.

The largest groups of insects are called *orders*. Sixteen orders of insects that include important pest species are summarized on page 7, as are the identifying characteristics of the other arthropod classes.

Orders are divided into *families* and the families into *genera* and *species*. An insect's scientific name usually consists of two words, its genus and species. The scientific names of the pests in this book are listed on pages 154–156. The common names used in the text are those approved by the Entomological Society of America.

MAJOR ORDERS OF INSECTS

CLASS	NAME OF ORDER	COMMON EXAMPLES	WINGS, MOUTHPARTS
INSECTA	Thysanura	silverfish, firebrats	wingless; chewing
	Collembola	springtails	wingless; chewing
	Orthoptera	grasshoppers, crickets, cockroaches	2 prs. wings or wingless; chewing
	Dermaptera	earwings	2 prs. wings or wingless; chewing
	Isoptera	termites	2 prs. wings or wingless; chewing
	Psocoptera	barklice, booklice	2 prs. wings or wingless; chewing
	Mallophaga	chewing lice	wingless; chewing
	Anoplura	sucking lice	2 prs. wings or wingless; piercing-sucking
	Thysanoptera	thrips	2 prs. wings or wingless; rasping-sucking
	Homoptera	aphids, leafhoppers scales, mealybugs	2 prs. wings or wingless; piercing-sucking
	Hemiptera	bed bugs, stink bugs, chinch bugs	wingless; piercing-sucking
	Coleoptera	beetles, weevils	2 prs. wings or wingless; chewing
	Lepidoptera	moths, butterflies	2 prs. wings; chewing (larvae), sucking, or siphoning (adults)
	Hymenoptera	wasps, bees, ants sawflies	2 prs. wings or wingless; chewing
	Diptera	mosquitoes, flies, gnats	1 pr. wings; chewing (larvae), piercing-sucking, or sponging (adults)
	Siphonaptera	fleas	wingless; chewing (larvae), piercing-sucking (adults)

CLASSES OF OTHER ARTHROPOD PESTS

ARACHNIDA	spiders, ticks, mites, scorpions	4 prs. legs; 2 body regions—cephalothorax and abdomen; no antennae; chewing or sucking mouthparts
CHILOPODA	centipedes	1 pr. of legs per body segment; 1 pr. of antennae; 2 body regions—head, trunk; body flattened; chewing mouthparts
DIPLOPODA	millipedes	2 prs. of legs per apparent body segment; 1 pr. of antennae; 2 body regions—head, trunk; body rounded; chewing mouthparts

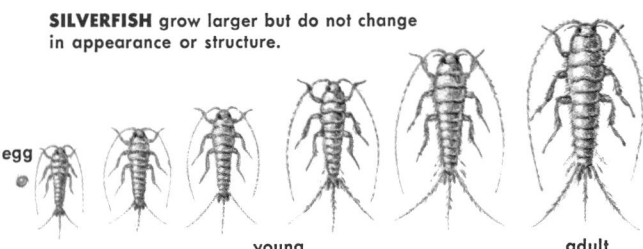

SILVERFISH grow larger but do not change in appearance or structure.

egg

young

adult

INSECT DEVELOPMENT An insect pest can be controlled most easily at a specific stage of its life history, sometimes not the one in which it does its greatest damage. Destroying the insect's eggs is often the most effective control measure. But to do this you must know where and when the female lays her eggs. Hence life histories are emphasized in this book.

Nymphs are young insects that, as soon as they hatch, resemble miniature adults. If the adult has wings, wing buds soon appear on the nymph's thorax. These grow each time the nymph sheds, or molts, and by the time the insect is mature, the wings are fully developed.

Nymphs are active. They commonly live in the same place and have the same feeding habits as the adults. True bugs, grasshoppers, cockroaches, and lice are among the insects that have a nymph stage. These change (metamorphose) gradually through three developmental stages—egg, nymph, and adult. This type of metamorphosis is called simple. Primitive insects, such as silverfish and springtails, also develop by a simple metamorphosis, but there are almost no changes in their structure as they grow, only an increase in size. Nymphs of some aquatic insects are called naiads; they differ considerably from adults in appearance and habits but change from naiads directly into adults.

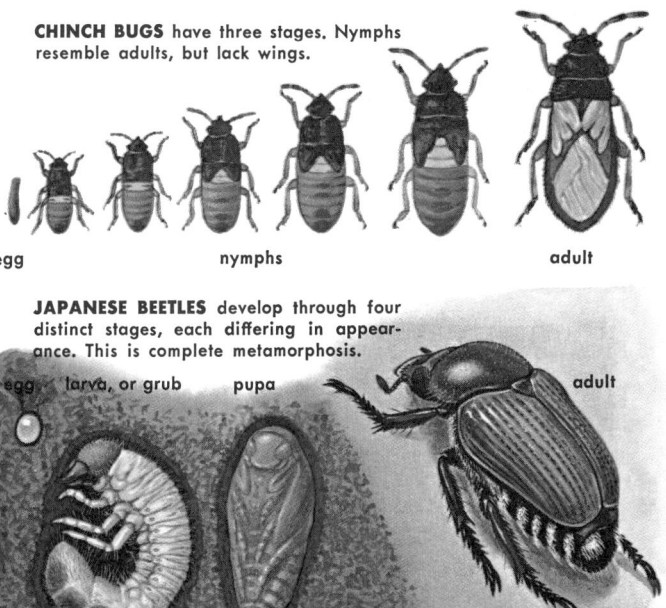

CHINCH BUGS have three stages. Nymphs resemble adults, but lack wings.

egg　　　　　　　nymphs　　　　　　　adult

JAPANESE BEETLES develop through four distinct stages, each differing in appearance. This is complete metamorphosis.

egg　larva, or grub　pupa　　　　　　　adult

More kinds of insects develop through a complete metamorphosis. The insect changes in appearance and habits from one stage to the next through four distinct stages—egg, larva, pupa, and adult. The egg hatches into a larva, an active, feeding stage. The mature larva forms a pupa, a resting, or nonfeeding, stage from which the insect emerges as an adult. Caterpillars are the crawling larvae of butterflies and moths. They have chewing mouthparts. Some are major pests of plants and stored products. The adults have sucking, or nectar-feeding, mouthparts and never do damage. Maggots are the larvae of flies; grubs, the larvae of beetles.

CONTROLLING INSECTS

Insects become pests when they damage crops, destroy products, transmit diseases, are annoying, or in other ways conflict with man's needs or interests. In man's continuous battle against insect pests through the centuries, no insect species has ever been eradicated, though some have been reduced in number, at least temporarily. At the same time, other pest species have actually become more abundant and are now a greater problem because man has provided increasingly favorable conditions for them. The modern one-crop system of agriculture often supplies food for an insect pest in large quantity over many square miles. As new crop plants were introduced from other countries, their insect pests often came with them, but not the predatory species that kept the pests under control in their homeland. Some varieties of crops are more susceptible to pests than were the original wild plants, which over the years developed a degree of resistance to insect attack.

NATURAL CONTROLS ordinarily keep insect populations in balance. Weather factors, such as temperature and rainfall, limit the distribution of an insect species, as do such geographic barriers as large bodies of water, deserts, or mountain ranges.

Toads, lizards, frogs, moles, and shrews are among the many animals that feed mainly on insects. Some birds may eat their own weight in insects every day. Predatory insects usually feed on whatever insects are available. Larvae of parasitic insects develop in the eggs, young, or adults of other insects. Virus, fungus, and bacterial diseases also help hold insect populations in check. Man has often upset these natural balances.

Because insect-eating birds tend to eat the most available insects, they are especially helpful in controlling pests in outbreaks.

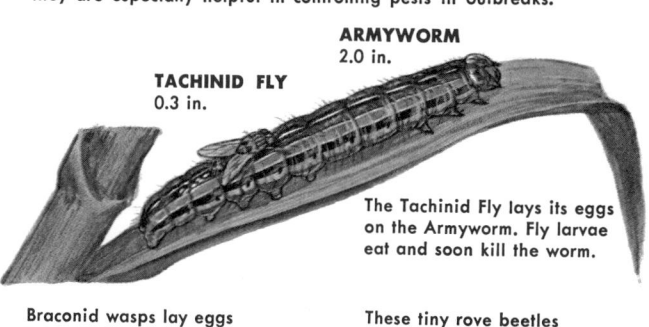

ARMYWORM
2.0 in.

TACHINID FLY
0.3 in.

The Tachinid Fly lays its eggs on the Armyworm. Fly larvae eat and soon kill the worm.

Braconid wasps lay eggs in aphids or other insects. Larvae develop inside.

These tiny rove beetles feed on maggots. The larvae also burrow into pupae.

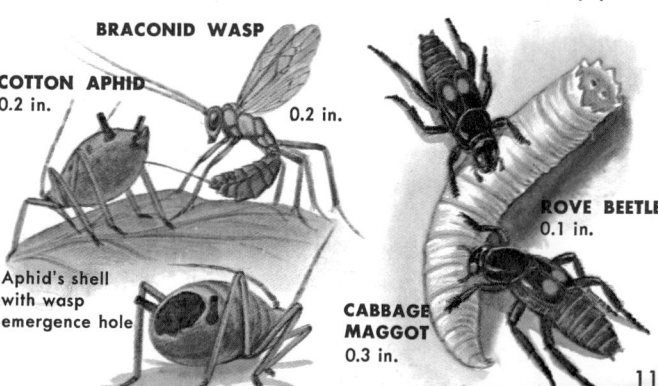

BRACONID WASP

COTTON APHID
0.2 in.

0.2 in.

Aphid's shell with wasp emergence hole

ROVE BEETLE
0.1 in.

CABBAGE MAGGOT
0.3 in.

11

BIOLOGICAL CONTROL is the purposeful use of natural predators, parasites, or diseases to kill or reduce the population of a pest species. This method has been effective principally in combating insect pests introduced from foreign countries without their natural enemies. Biological controls are not usually practical for home gardens or similar small areas. They are used most successfully in orchards and groves or where large-scale crop plantings are repeated year after year on the same land. Usually the control species is at first bred artificially so that it can be introduced in large numbers. More than two dozen cases of effective large-scale control of insect pests have been achieved by this method.

Damage to citrus by the Cottony-cushion Scale in California was virtually eliminated by the introduction of Vedalia, an Australian lady beetle. Later, grove

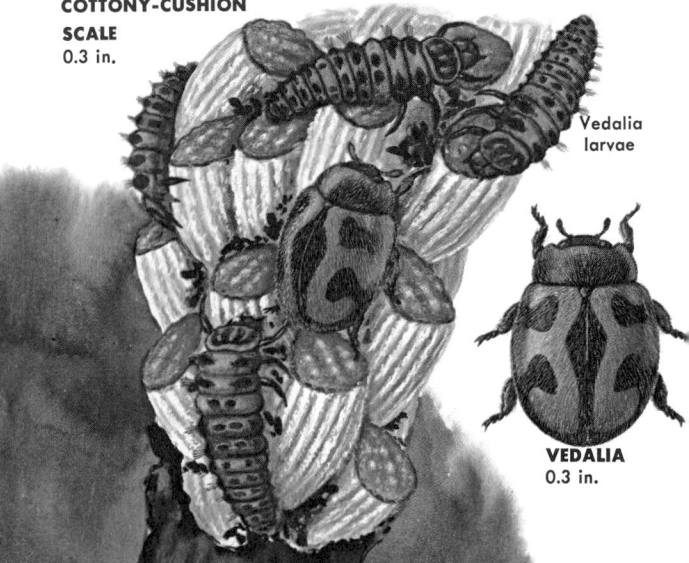

COTTONY-CUSHION SCALE
0.3 in.

Vedalia larvae

VEDALIA
0.3 in.

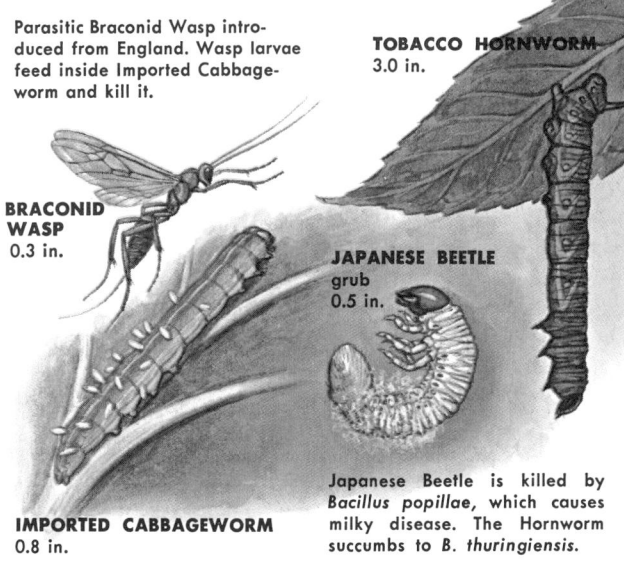

Parasitic Braconid Wasp introduced from England. Wasp larvae feed inside Imported Cabbageworm and kill it.

BRACONID WASP
0.3 in.

TOBACCO HORNWORM
3.0 in.

JAPANESE BEETLE
grub
0.5 in.

IMPORTED CABBAGEWORM
0.8 in.

Japanese Beetle is killed by *Bacillus popillae*, which causes milky disease. The Hornworm succumbs to *B. thuringiensis*.

owners began to spray their trees to kill aphids. At the same time they killed the Vedalia beetles, causing an outbreak of Cottony-cushion Scale again. The use of bacteria causing milky disease that kills grubs of the Japanese Beetle is another example of successful biological control. Gambusias and other top-feeding minnows are effective in the control of mosquito larvae. Interestingly, the Chrysolina Beetle was introduced to western United States from Australia to halt the spread of the Klamath weed.

Biological controls do not eliminate a pest species completely. They only reduce the population and thus keep the damage low. But biological controls are usually self-generating, so a control species, once established, continues to reproduce and to remain effective.

13

PHYSICAL AND MECHANICAL CONTROLS are the simplest, most obvious, and at times most effective: witness the old-fashioned fly swatter. Pests of stored products are commonly destroyed by heat or cold. Few can survive long in a temperature of 120 degrees F. or higher. Cold either kills or stops activity. Draining off standing water to eliminate breeding places is a standard mosquito control method, while many plant pests are killed by flooding. Lights are used to attract some kinds of pests, which may then be electrocuted on charged screens. Pests that collect in large numbers may be lured to baits or caught in ditches. The gardener who picks Japanese Beetles off his roses by hand uses an effective method for small areas.

CULTURAL CONTROL is an inexpensive method of checking or preventing damage by insect pests by combining mechanical or physical controls with a knowledge of the pest's life history. Crop rotation prevents the build-up of a pest population that feeds on one kind of plant. Burying stalks, weeds, and other residues after harvest destroys eggs, pupae, or hibernating larvae and adults. Similarly, early or late plowing may destroy a particular life stage of a pest. Planting and harvesting can sometimes be timed to escape periods of egg laying or of pest abundance. Varieties of plants resistant to particular pests can be planted. Healthy, vigorously growing plants can withstand insect attacks better than those that are weak or diseased. Likewise, animals in good health are not as greatly disturbed by pests.

Golden Regent, a resistant variety of sweet corn.

Spancross, a variety susceptible to Corn Earworm.

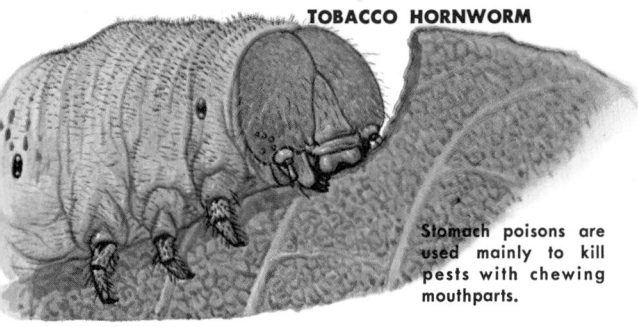

TOBACCO HORNWORM

Stomach poisons are used mainly to kill pests with chewing mouthparts.

INSECTICIDES are poisons used to kill insect pests. Their great advantage is speed. Biological control methods, while safer and longer lasting, may require several seasons to become effective.

More than 350 million pounds of insecticides are sold annually in the United States. Their use increases agricultural yields by an average of about 25 percent and in many cases prevents complete crop losses. Insecticides are highly important, too, in the control of pests that are annoying or are disease carriers.

Most insecticides are dangerous to people and other animals as well as to pests. Read and follow carefully the instruction on labels. Consult a county agent or an entomologist or employ the services of a professional pest-control operator.

TARNISHED PLANT BUG

Pests with sucking mouthparts are killed with contact poisons.

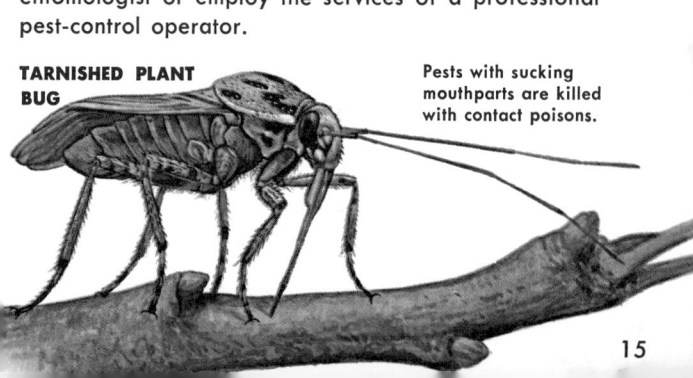

APPLICATIONS of insecticides are rarely made full strength. *Dusts* are dry mixtures of from 0.1 percent to 25 percent of the poison mixed with fine particles of an inactive material, such as talc. *Wettable powders* are dusts that form a suspension in water for spraying; the powder may consist of from 10 to 95 percent insecticide. *Emulsifiable concentrates,* the most common formulation for applying insecticides, consist of oil or a similar organic solvent containing the insecticide and an emulsifier that aids the mixing of the droplets of oil and insecticide in water. The components may separate on standing but can be remixed by shaking. *Special solvents,* such as kerosene, pine oil, and other liquids of organic compounds, are used with the water-insoluble organic insecticides. Most solvents are toxic to plants, are inflammable, and may damage wallpaper, tile, and other materials. For all applications, follow printed directions with care.

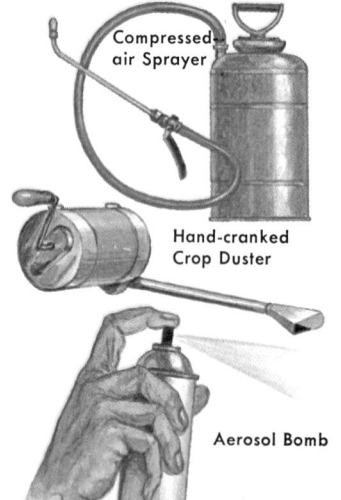

Compressed-air Sprayer

Hand-cranked Crop Duster

Aerosol Bomb

SPRAYERS use a pump to build up air pressure that forces the liquid insecticide from the nozzle. The size of the nozzle opening creates either a foglike mist or a steady stream.

DUSTERS are powered by hand or by motor and use either a fan or compressed air to force out the dust in a cloud.

AEROSOL BOMBS, the most common household applicators, consist of an insecticide dissolved in a liquefied gas under high pressure. A fine mist is produced when these are allowed to escape from a small opening. Aerosols are convenient but are relatively expensive.

Bean beetles and their larvae (p. 76) feed on the underside of leaves. They can be reached with insecticide dusts.

STOMACH POISONS are used principally to kill insects with chewing mouthparts. They may be sprayed or dusted directly on the insect's food or may be mixed with baits to attract the pests. To be useful a stomach poison must kill fairly quickly, as the pest is already doing damage when it takes in the insecticide. Too heavy an application of these chemicals may kill the plants. The residues are poisonous to man and domestic animals. Contact insecticides (p. 18) act as stomach poisons if eaten. Arsenic compounds are the most common inorganic stomach poisons. *Paris green* (calcium acetoarsenite) was the first chemical insecticide used successfully on a large scale. *Lead arsenate, white arsenic* (arsenious oxide), *sodium arsenate,* and *calcium arsenate* are other arsenic stomach poisons. Fluorine compounds that act as stomach poisons are *sodium fluosilicate, sodium fluoride,* and *sodium fluoaluminate* (cryolite). *Thallium sulfate,* highly poisonous, is mixed with food to make ant baits. Do not store any insecticide where children can reach it. Make certain the containers are properly labeled and marked POISON.

CONTACT INSECTICIDES are sprayed or dusted directly on pests or are spread where pests will pick them up. They are especially useful in controlling insects with piercing-sucking mouthparts. All contact poisons act as stomach poisons (p. 17) if eaten. Most of them are also poisonous to people and animals and thus are a serious hazard if not used as directed. In excess amounts many contact insecticides are poisonous to plants. Some are used as fumigants. Always read the label before even opening the insecticide container. When in doubt about how to use an insecticide safely and most effectively, ask the advice of your dealer or of a county or agricultural agent.

Most of the many thousands of tradenamed insecticide formulations belong in the contact-insecticide group. These are divided into the following groups— *inorganics, natural organics* or *plant poisons, synthetics,* and *oils.* Each of these groups is described separately on the following pages. Most of the contact insecticides now used have appeared since the World War II development of DDT, the first widely used synthetic organic insecticide.

INORGANIC CONTACT INSEC- TICIDES, consisting mainly of *sulfur dusts,* mixtures of *lime* and *sulfur,* or *sulfur compounds,* were the first contact poisons used on a large scale and still rank among the most important. *Sulfur dust* is one of the main chemical controls for mites, for the crawling stages of scales, and for some kinds of caterpillars. Finely ground sulfur is usable as a wettable powder for spray applications. *Lime-sulfur solution* is a liquid, soluble in water. Lime-sulfur is also dehydrated and sold in concentrated powder form. It is used to control plant pests such as scales and also as a dip for cattle, sheep, and other livestock. *Bordeaux mixture* is a combination of copper sulfate and lime in water. In addition to their use as insecticides, sulfur and sulfur compounds are valued as fungicides. In hot weather, heavy applications of sulfur will burn foliage and fruit and so must be applied sparingly.

NATURAL ORGANICS were the earliest compounds used in killing insect pests. With the exception of nicotine, highly toxic to man and other mammals, they are the least dangerous of the insecticides to use on food plants or in the house.

Nicotine is obtained from the waste leaves of tobacco plants and waste tobacco products. It is used principally as *nicotine sulfate*, with a 40-percent nicotine content. The 40-percent concentrate is ordinarily diluted in 800 to 1,000 parts of water (about one teaspoon to a gallon) and is applied as a spray to kill aphids or other soft-bodied insects. Nicotine sulfate is used also as a stock dip for control of mites, ticks, and lice. Finely ground tobacco stems and leaves are used as a dust or burned as a fumigant. Nicotine may be added to aerosol formulations.

Pyrethrum comes from the flowers of several species of chrysanthemums. It is produced commercially from a species grown in East Africa. Fast-acting pyrethrins are the "knockdown" agents in most household sprays, with slower-acting DDT or other synthetics actually killing the insect. *Allethrin,* produced synthetically, is much the same as pyrethrum in action.

Rotenone is obtained from the dried and ground roots of the South American cubé and from the roots of two species of derris that grow in the East Indies. As prepared for an insecticide,

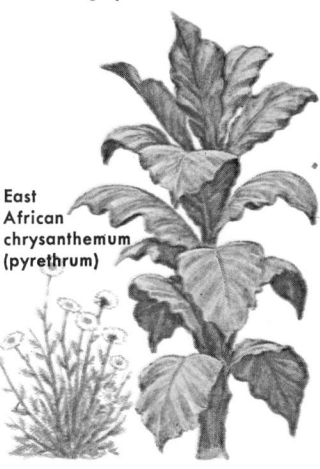

Tobacco plant, source of highly toxic nicotine

East African chrysanthemum (pyrethrum)

rotenone is relatively nontoxic to humans, but as an insecticide it acts both as a stomach and as a contact poison. Another use of rotenone by biologists is as a poison to eliminate trash fish in lakes and ponds.

Other botanicals, or natural-organic contact insecticides, include *ryania,* produced from the pulverized stems and roots of a South American plant. Ryania is less toxic to mammals than rotenone and so is recommended for food plants where residues might be a problem. *Sabadilla,* which also has low toxicity, is made by grinding the seeds of a lily-family plant of Venezuela.

SYNTHETIC ORGANIC CONTACT INSECTICIDES are the most important group of chemicals used today in the control of insect pests. There are two groups: chlorinated hydrocarbons and organo-phosphates.

CHLORINATED HYDROCARBONS

DDT is the leader in the chlorinated hydrocarbon group. Though first synthesized in 1874, DDT was not recognized as an insecticide until World War II, when its initial large-scale use halted a typhus epidemic spread by lice in Italy. It was later valuable during the war years in the control of flies and mosquitoes and came into widespread use in the control of agricultural and household pests after the war. DDT is highly effective in killing many kinds of insects but is relatively nontoxic to aphids, spider mites, and some other species. Some cockroaches, flies, and other insects have developed resistance to DDT. When an insect comes in contact with DDT, it first appears to lose control of its voluntary actions; later it becomes paralyzed. Death comes slowly, sometimes several days later. DDT has a rather low toxicity to man and other vertebrates but may be stored in the fatty tissues of the body and cause death months later when the fat reserves are utilized.

DDT is applied as a dust, wettable powder, water emulsion, or in an oil base. Vertebrates absorb the oil-base DDT most rapidly. DDT is insoluble in water. Its residues may remain effective outdoors for many months or even years, indoors for even longer. *Methoxychlor*, related to DDT, is effective against the Mexican Bean Beetle and works more rapidly in killing the House Fly. *TDE* (or DDD), also a relative of DDT, is commonly used in mosquito control because it is less toxic than DDT to vertebrates. TDE is also less poisonous to insects, however.

Benzene hexachloride (BHC), also in the chlorinated-hydrocarbon group, was discovered as a useful insecticide about the same time as DDT. BHC kills faster than DDT and is commonly used in the control of crop pests. It has a distinctive musty odor and sometimes taints food. BHC is usually used as a dust or a wettable powder. *Lindane* is BHC that differs only in the arrangement of its atoms, but as it lacks the objectionable heavy odor, it is used more commonly in houses. Though its residual life is shorter than DDT's, lindane is about twice as toxic to many insects and apparently is not stored in the body tissues. *Toxaphene*, insoluble in water but soluble in many organic solvents, is an excellent insect killer but is also poisonous to vertebrates. Toxaphene is one of the most common insecticides for controlling pests of cotton.

Chlordane, dieldrin, aldrin, endrin, and *heptachlor* form another group of closely related chlorinated hydrocarbons. All are insoluble in water but are soluble in many organic solvents.

Scales may be killed with organo-phosphate sprays (below and p. 86). Use these insecticides with great care.

ROSE SCALE
0.3 in.

They are also used in dust or pellet form, particularly as soil poisons for the control of termites and ants. They are highly effective insect killers and are residual. They are also poisonous to vertebrates, including man and other mammals.

ORGANO-PHOSPHATES

The organo-phosphate group of contact insecticides stems from chemical research just before World War II, when some of these compounds were developed as poisonous gases for use in warfare. Most of them are extremely lethal to man and animals as well as to insects. They can be taken into the body through the mouth or the skin or by inhaling their fumes. Residues on foods are a source of danger. Because these insecticides are very poisonous, they must be handled with the greatest care.

Parathion, a brownish-yellow liquid with a garlic odor, is too poisonous for household use or for applying near livestock and pets, but it is widely used on fruit and vegetable crops. Residues disappear rapidly. *Demeton*, about as poisonous as parathion, acts as a systemic poison, being absorbed by the tissues of the plant. It kills pests that feed on the plant's juices without affecting predators and pollinators. *TEPP*, even more poisonous than parathion, decomposes rapidly and leaves no residue. It is used regularly on food crops.

Malathion, most commonly used organo-phosphate, is not highly toxic to vertebrates. Malathion will kill many insect species that have developed a resistance to the insecticides of the DDT and chlordane groups. *Diazinon*, *DDVP*, *ronnel*, and *dicapthon* are other organo-phosphates that are excellent insect killers. DDVP is the most highly toxic of these chemicals to man and animals.

Oils are applied to citrus to kill young stages of Purple Scale (p. 133) and Citrus Whitefly (p. 136).

OILS, principally petroleum but also some animal and vegetable oils, serve as carriers for insecticides or may be used as insecticides themselves. *Dormant oils*, rather heavy and semirefined, are applied in late winter or early spring to trees or shrubs that are not in foliage to kill scales, mites, eggs, and some larvae. *Summer oils* are lighter and more highly refined, hence less damaging to plants; they are used to control aphids, scale insects, and mealybugs. As the oils themselves are toxic to plants if applied full strength, they are mixed with water by adding an emulsifier, such as soap. This distributes the oil evenly as small droplets. Oil baths may be used to kill such parasites as fleas, lice, ticks, and mites on domestic animals and pets. Formulations that require shaking with a small amount of water before final mixing are called *miscible* oils. An *emulsible*-oil formulation can be poured directly into the water.

FUMIGANTS are gases used to kill insects in enclosures, as in buildings or containers, in the soil, or under such temporary covers as tarpaulins and tents. Many fumigants are inflammable. Nearly all fumigants are more poisonous to man than to the insects and should be used only by a professional pest-control operator. Their advantage is their penetration to all parts of buildings, into stored products or plants. They leave no residue. *Carbon disulfide* (carbon bisulfide), highly inflammable, is used mainly as a soil fumigant for ants, termites, and grubs. For indoor use it may be mixed with carbon tetrachloride to reduce the danger of fire or explosion. *Dichloropropene* and *dichloropropane* are also used as soil fumigants. *Hydrogen cyanide*, which has a distinctive nutty odor and is deadly poisonous, is used to fumigate mills and warehouses or fruit trees under tents. *Methyl bromide*, a noninflammable fumigant, is valued because of its power to penetrate tightly packed materials. *Paradichlorobenzene* ("para" crystals) and *naphthalene* (both sold as mothballs) vaporize slowly and act as a fumigant and a repellent.

REPELLENTS are chemicals that by their odor or taste prevent insect attacks. They are used mainly to protect man, animals, or stored products; less commonly, plants. Some repellents are poisonous if touched, eaten, or breathed. *Mothballs* are repellents that protect clothes from insect damage. *Creosote* is used as a barrier against crawling insects, while *smoke screens* ward off flies and mosquitoes. Among the most successful of dozens of repellent chemicals are *diethyl toluamide, dimethyl phthalate,* and *ethyl hexanediol.* These organic chemicals are diluted with oils and disguised with perfumes. They are sold under many tradenames. Most will repel insects for one to five hours.

NEW METHODS of combating insect pests are being developed every year. Some are useful only in large-scale control programs, others in home and garden. Among the most promising are *sterilants* that render insects incapable of reproducing. This method was first used with success to control the Screw-worm. Millions of males, sterilized by radiation, were released in areas of infestation to mate with females, which then produced infertile eggs. *Hormones* are used to cause an insect to pass from one stage of its development to the next irrespective of season. Thus, pupae can be made to transform into adults in midwinter or larvae may be made to pupate before they are full grown. Insect hormones are apparently harmless to other living things. Also safe are such *nontoxic insecticides* as finely ground silica, which abrades the outer covering from an insect and causes it to dry up, or desiccate, as its body fluids escape.

The soil in seed beds can be fumigated by releasing methyl-bromide gas under plastic cover.

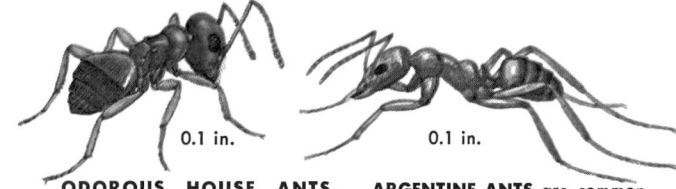

ODOROUS HOUSE ANTS, widespread in U.S., give off a sweet odor when crushed. Travel definite trails to find food.

ARGENTINE ANTS are common in southern U.S.; worst ant pests in houses. Prefer sweets but eat all foods. Bite, do not sting.

HOUSEHOLD PESTS

Insect pests may destroy the timbers of a house, tunnel into furniture and fabrics, or raid the contents of the kitchen, from the spice cabinet to the garbage pail. Some kinds bite, sting, or transmit diseases. Others are simply annoying, uninvited guests.

The basic step in controlling household pests is to keep them out. Screen windows and doors, seal cracks, and remove debris in which pests can hide or multiply. If pest infestations are heavy, persistent, or unexplainable, services of a professional pest-control operator may be necessary. Make certain the man employed represents a licensed, bonded organization.

Many pests can be recognized and controlled without expert help. Since insecticides are poisonous and will be used where there are people, pets, and food, follow carefully the directions given on the label.

THIEF ANTS often live in other ant nests and feed on larvae. They prefer cheese, meats, or other greasy food.

PHARAOH ANTS also like meat. May nest in walls and then invade all parts of house. Poison baits are best control method.

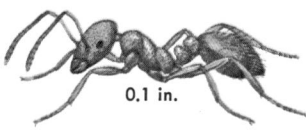

0.1 in. 0.1 in.

CRAZY ANTS, native to India but now widespread, run "crazily" on their long legs. They eat meat, greasy foods, and sweets.

CORNFIELD ANTS are the common "red ants" of northern states. Nest mounds often numerous on lawns. Invade houses.

ANTS live in colonies in the ground, in the foundations or walls of buildings, beneath bark or stones. A colony contains numerous workers (sterile females), one to several queens, and a few males during part of the year. Workers do not have wings, but males and females are winged at swarming time. Males die after mating, and the queens drop their wings and find a place to start a colony. After mating, queens remain fertile, living as long as 25 years. Queens are usually several times larger than workers, which attend their every need. Ants belong to same insect order as bees and wasps. They have elbowed antennae and a thin waist, distinguishing them from termites (p. 26).

The most effective control is to destroy the nest if it can be found. Chemical barriers, using a residual contact insecticide, can be placed around foundations of buildings. Workers will carry poisoned baits to the colony and thus kill even the queen.

SOUTHERN FIRE ANTS occur in warm parts of U.S. Often nest near buildings. Invade houses. Stings are painful.

BLACK CARPENTER ANTS excavate galleries and nest in wood. They enter houses to get sweets. Bite but do not sting.

0.4 in. 0.4 in.

TERMITES are primitive social insects, more closely related to cockroaches (p. 28) than to ants (p. 25). A colony consists of numerous whitish, wingless, blind *workers;* a lesser number of *soldiers,* with large brownish heads equipped with powerful jaws or with a bellows-shaped snout that expels a sticky or odorous fluid; and *reproductives,* the king and queen. Additional winged males and females are produced for swarming, which takes place in spring or after rains in warm weather. After a short flight they break off their wings and mate. Each mated pair then crawls off in search of a suitable place to establish a new colony.

More than 50 species of termites occur in the U.S. Their spread as far north as Minnesota in recent years is attributed to increased use of central heating in buildings, enabling them to survive winters. Nearly all U.S. species live in the soil; many of the more than 2,000 species of the tropics build aboveground nests.

Termites eat wood but cannot absorb it until the cellulose is converted into soluble substances by protozoans that live in the termite's digestive tract. Neither animal is able to survive alone.

damaged wood

termite tubes up foundation

metal shield
on foundation

SUBTERRANEAN TERMITES live in colonies in soil, and workers travel through tunnels or mud tubes to the wood above. Fungi that grow in moist, dark tunnels are eaten by termites, supplying protein and vitamins.

Swarming flights or mud tubes up a foundation are evidence of a termite infestation. In late stages, floors sag as eaten-out beams crumble.

To control, no wood of a building should touch soil. Preventive measures should be taken as a building is being constructed. Place metal shields between the foundation and sills and allow air to circulate under buildings. Because of the special equipment needed, use a professional pest-control operator, especially in treating a building already erected. He will force penetrating insecticide into the wood or foundation, treat the soil beneath buildings, or use a fumigant. Inspect regularly to detect renewed activity.

worker 0.2 in. reproductive 0.5 in.

DRYWOOD TERMITES are prevalent in the southwestern U.S. No contact with soil is necessary. Often they invade a house at roof level and may infest furniture or books. Piles of brownish, seedlike excrement pellets pushed from tunnels are signs of their presence. Preventing entry is not economical. Control, which should be done only by experts, consists of forcing insecticide into tunnels. Poison is spread as workers groom each other. House or infested object may be fumigated, but this does not prevent reinfestation.

EASTERN SUBTERRANEAN TERMITE

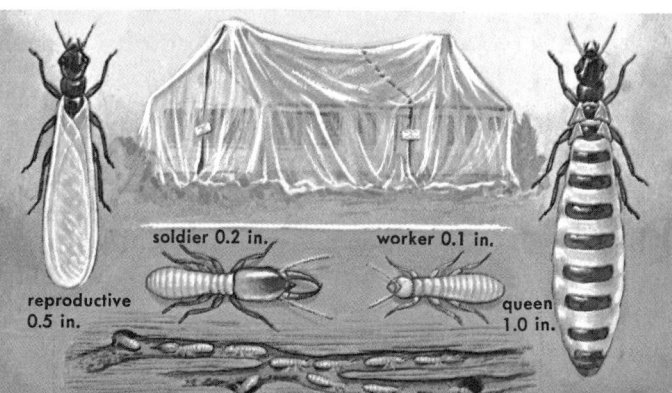

reproductive 0.5 in.

soldier 0.2 in.

worker 0.1 in.

queen 1.0 in.

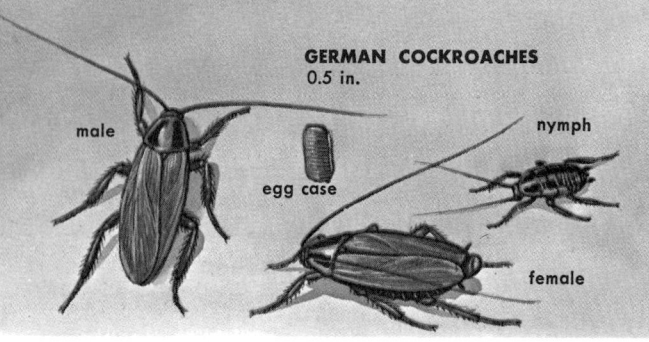

GERMAN COCKROACHES
0.5 in.

male

egg case

nymph

female

COCKROACHES feed on a great variety of foods—meats, cheeses, sweets, and starches, including the starch in clothing or in the glue of book bindings and stamps: When very abundant, they may also eat human hair, skin, and nails. Cockroaches secrete a sticky, odorous fluid that may be left on foods or materials. Fortunately, cockroaches appear to be only incidental carriers of diseases.

Most of the more than 3,000 species of cockroaches live in the tropics or subtropics. About 55 occur in the U.S.; only four species are common household pests.

Normally cockroaches are active only at night. They develop by a gradual metamorphosis—egg, nymph, and adult. Egg cases contain two rows of eggs, and the nymphs escape through a seam along the side. Nymphs look like adults but lack wings and may be a lighter color. After a period of growth and several molts they become adults. The time required for them to mature varies with the species and also with the season and the region. Temperature and moisture as well as food are important factors in their development.

The best permanent control for cockroaches is eliminating accessibility of foods which they eat.

GERMAN COCKROACHES, or Croton Bugs, are common in U.S., especially in northern states. Dark stripes on shield behind head are distinguishing. Both sexes winged and active.

German Cockroaches commonly enter houses in bags or boxes from grocery stores. They tend to cluster in warm, moist places, as around hot-water pipes, and stay hidden when not feeding.

Females carry the egg capsule, containing 24 to 48 eggs, until hatching time. Nymphs may emerge while the capsule is still attached to the female.

In most areas German Cockroaches are resistant to DDT, chlordane, and other chlorinated hydrocarbons. They can be controlled with organo-phosphates, such as malathion.

BROWN-BANDED COCK-ROACH has two light bands across the base of its wings. Unlike other cockroaches, it is as common in the bedroom as in the kitchen, requiring warmth but not as much moisture. Control is difficult because these cockroaches are found so widely through the house. The most effective way to reach them is with fumigants, keeping room or house closed for several hours.

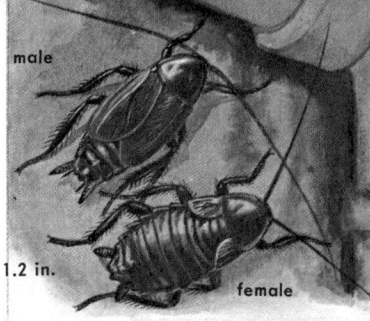

male
1.2 in.
female

ORIENTAL COCKROACHES, also called Black Beetles or Water Bugs, are most sluggish of domestic cockroaches. Females have short useless wings and are slightly larger than males. Commonly infest damp basements. Contact-insecticide barrier around a foundation blocks entry of these cockroaches and other crawling pests.

AMERICAN COCKROACHES are the largest cockroaches in the U.S. Both sexes are winged, their flight gliding and fluttery. The female deposits her egg capsule soon after it forms, sometimes gluing it to a surface. In the South these cockroaches are common outdoors, where they live under bark or in vegetation. They can be controlled with contact insecticides or lured to poison baits.

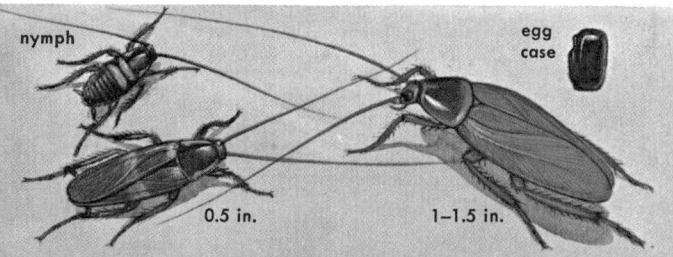

nymph
egg case
0.5 in.
1–1.5 in.

CLOTHES MOTH larvae feed on woolen fabrics, feathers, fur, mohair, and other animal products such as dried milk and meals. The adult moths, commonly called "millers," do not eat, and unlike most other moths, are not attracted to lights.

Material likely to be attacked should be cleaned and exposed frequently to light. Brushing clothes dislodges the eggs and larvae. Storage of furs at a temperature of 45 degrees or cooler prevents development of moths or will kill them if the temperature is raised and lowered several times during the storage period. Items can be sprayed with residual contact insecticides or washables rinsed in an insecticide solution. These treatments kill the insects as they feed. Mild fumigants such as para-dichlorobenzene crystals or naphthalene flakes discourage moth attacks. These insecticides will also kill moths already in the fabrics but are effective only when used in tight containers or closets. An infestation may persist and spread from larvae that feed and develop on lint in cracks in the floor, beneath baseboards, or in vents. In heavy infestations an entire house may be fumigated. This should be done only by a professional exterminator.

DERMESTID BEETLES are pests of fabrics and upholstered furniture and also infest cured meats, meals, cheeses, hides, hair, flour or other grain products, and spices. They are serious pests in museums. Outdoors they are valuable as scavengers. Larvae of dermestid beetles are more active than the larvae of clothes moths. Adults fly in daytime. They commonly feed on the pollen of flowers and also breed outdoors. Treatments effective for clothes moths also control carpet beetles. In both cases, good housekeeping to eliminate breeding places is the most important preventive.

WEBBING CLOTHES MOTHS are common fabric pests that occur throughout the world. Females lay eggs about 0.02 of an inch long (barely visible), either singly or in small groups, sticking them to the threads of fabrics. Eggs hatch in a few days to several weeks, depending on temperature and humidity. The larvae are so tiny they can crawl between the woven threads of fabrics. They spin a silky webbing or tunnel as they feed, sometimes moving to another spot if their food runs short. Damage is most common under collars, in cuffs, or in other dark areas of garments. Full-grown larvae spin a silken cocoon from which they emerge as adults in three to six weeks.

CASEMAKING CLOTHES MOTH larvae spin a case of silk and fabric, carrying it with them as they feed. The case splits and the "V" of the split is filled in as the larva grows. Common in northern states. Plaster Bagworms of southern states build a portable case of bits of plaster or fabric woven into the silk of the case.

CARPET BEETLES, also called Buffalo Beetles, are dermestids that infest woolen fabrics, feathers, and other animal products. Related pests include the larger Hide Beetle and the Larder Beetle. Hides and skins are treated with arsenic powders or similar stomach poisons. Cheese, cured meats, and other fatty foods should be kept in tight containers or under refrigeration.

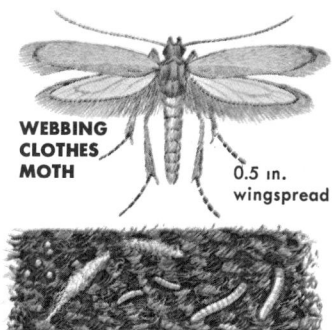

WEBBING CLOTHES MOTH

0.5 in. wingspread

eggs, larvae and cocoons on fabric.

CASEMAKING CLOTHES MOTH

larva in case 0.3 in.

larva 0.3 in.

PLASTER BAGWORM

1. **LARDER BEETLE,** 0.3 in.; 2. **CARPET BEETLE,** 0.2 in.; 3. **HIDE BEETLE,** 0.3 in.

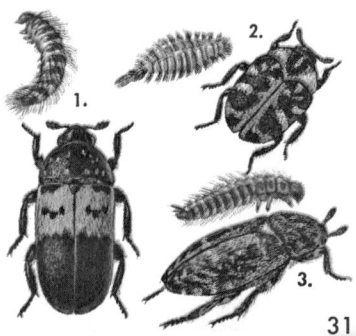

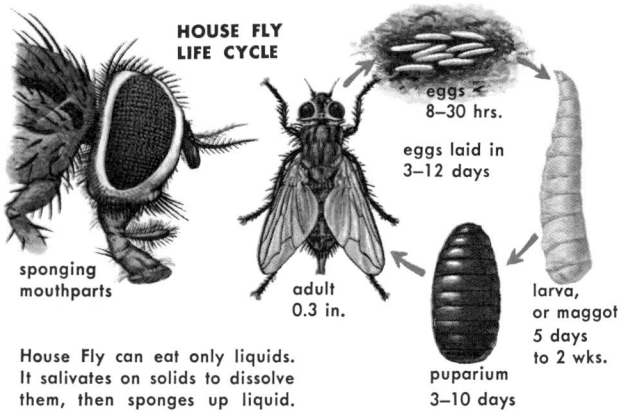

HOUSE FLY LIFE CYCLE

eggs
8–30 hrs.

eggs laid in
3–12 days

sponging
mouthparts

adult
0.3 in.

larva,
or maggot
5 days
to 2 wks.

puparium
3–10 days

House Fly can eat only liquids.
It salivates on solids to dissolve
them, then sponges up liquid.

HOUSE FLIES are bothersome, dangerous pests, transmitting diseases and parasites from the filth in which they breed to the foods man eats. Females may lay half a dozen or more clusters of 100 to 150 eggs in a season. In favorable conditions a life cycle is completed in about two weeks but may take many months in cold weather. Winter is ordinarily passed in the larva or pupa stage, but adults may overwinter in warm niches. Disposal of garbage, manure, sewage, and similar decaying or fermenting wastes in which the flies breed and the maggots develop is most important. Windows and doors should be fitted with tight screens. Flies that enter can be killed with aerosol sprays. Walls, sills, and screens can be treated with residual surface sprays. As flies in most areas are resistant to DDT, other contact insecticides must be substituted. Poison baits (mixtures of syrup- or sugar-water with an insecticide) are effective in places that cannot be screened or where sprays cannot be used because of danger of contamination.

LITTLE HOUSE FLIES are smaller and more slender than the House Fly. They hover or fly back and forth without settling on food. The similar, closely related Latrine Fly breeds in human excrement. Maggots of both have a flattened, spiny body.

BLOW FLIES are large and noisy. Most species are metallic blue or green, like the Green Bottle and Blue Bottle flies shown here. The gray Cluster Fly, similar in appearance to House Fly, is a blow fly common in houses. Blow fly maggots develop in garbage or carrion.

MOTH FLIES, their wings and body covered with hair, often appear in sink or bathtub drains. The maggots develop in the gelatinous sludge in the bends of pipes. Sometimes large numbers invade from outdoors, where they develop in garbage or sewage. They are so tiny they can crawl through screens.

FRUIT FLIES can enter houses through ordinary screens. They are attracted to rotting or fermenting fruits or liquids. A complete life cycle requires less than two weeks. Other common names for them are Vinegar Flies or Pomace Flies.

LITTLE HOUSE FLY

larva

adult
0.2 in.

GREEN BOTTLE FLY
0.5 in.

BLUE BOTTLE FLY
0.5 in.

CLUSTER FLY
0.3 in.

MOTH FLY 0.2 in.

GNAT is a name used for many kinds of small flies, most of which are only nuisances. The Eye Gnat, attracted to eye secretions, transmits pinkeye. These persistent tormentors are most active in early morning or evening hours.

DROSOPHILA FRUIT FLY

EYE GNAT

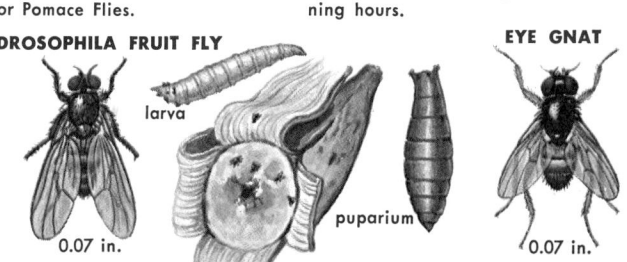

larva

puparium

0.07 in.

0.07 in.

MANY OTHER KINDS of insects, as well as spiders, and their kin enter houses, where they are either nuisances or potentially dangerous pests. Some of these are discussed in the section on insects that bite or sting (p. 38), others in the section on stored products (p. 146). Often an invasion of insects is only temporary, as when they are attracted to lights. When a lawn is mowed, a vacant lot is cleaned up, or a crop is harvested nearby, insects disturbed from their normal living places may be temporary pests. Others are regular visitors and companions in dwellings.

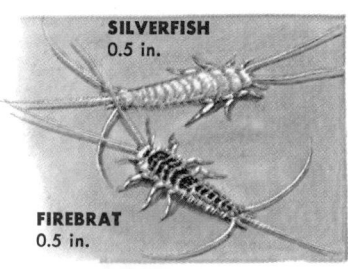

SILVERFISH
0.5 in.

FIREBRAT
0.5 in.

SILVERFISH are scaly, wingless insects that prefer foods with a high starch or sugar content. They eat the glue in book bindings or from wallpaper and often damage paintings or paper. Silverfish prefer cool, damp places; the closely related Firebrat lives in warm, drier spots. Residual sprays or dusts are effective in keeping down infestations.

EUROPEAN EARWIG
0.6 in.

female brooding young

EARWIGS are easily recognized by forceps at end of abdomen. Sometimes occur in large numbers in houses. They can bite and also pinch, but seldom break the skin. They hide during the day, feed at night. Use residual sprays or dusts.

HOUSE CRICKET
0.8 in.

HOUSE CRICKETS sing on the hearth or wherever they can find warmth. When cold, they are sluggish and quiet. Field Crickets also enter houses in autumn. As house pests, crickets eat a variety of foods and may be destructive to clothes. Household sprays, dusts, and poison baits are usually effective.

WOOD-BORING BEETLES of a number of species may infest wood used in houses or furniture. Larvae of the Southern Lyctus Beetle reduce wood to a fine powder, which is pushed outside through small holes. Droppings of the Furniture Beetle and others are round pellets. As some kinds feed, a ticking noise in the wood can be heard. Fumigation by a qualified pest-control operator is the best control.

BOOKLICE, or Psocids, sometimes become abundant in stored furniture, books, or papers, particularly if damp. They feed mainly on molds but also eat cereals. Booklice are so small that it is difficult to keep them out of a house. Use contact sprays or dusts.

BOXELDER BUGS do not bite, sting, or carry diseases, but are annoyances when large numbers occur near or in houses. Can be killed with household sprays.

CRANE FLIES look like large mosquitoes but are harmless. Their larvae, or maggots, sometimes called leatherjackets, develop in damp vegetation or in the soil. Adults commonly are attracted to the lights in houses. They can be killed with household fly sprays.

SPRINGTAILS often congregate in cellars or in bathrooms or kitchens, wherever there is dampness. They are harmless and can be killed with household sprays or dusts.

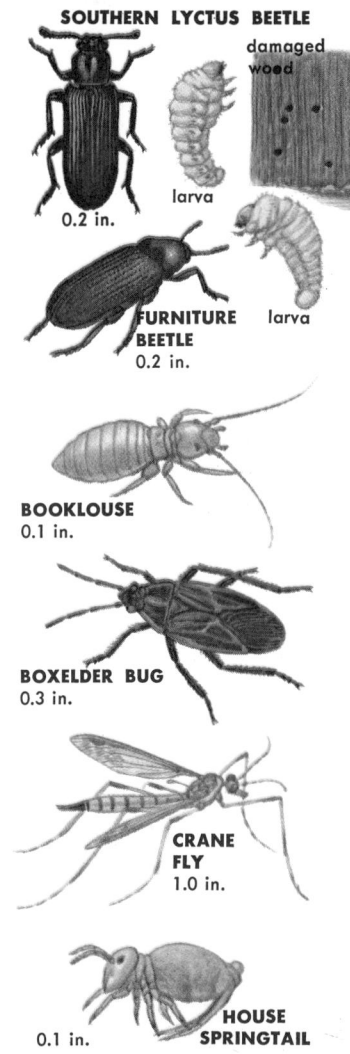

SOUTHERN LYCTUS BEETLE

damaged wood

larva
0.2 in.

FURNITURE BEETLE
0.2 in.
larva

BOOKLOUSE
0.1 in.

BOXELDER BUG
0.3 in.

CRANE FLY
1.0 in.

HOUSE SPRINGTAIL
0.1 in.

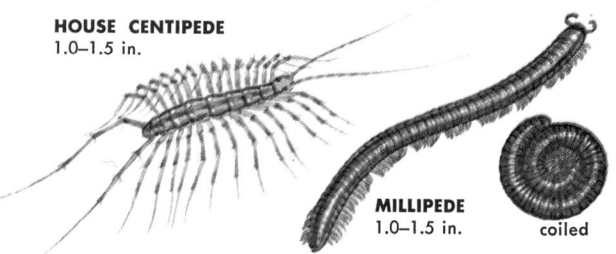

HOUSE CENTIPEDE
1.0–1.5 in.

MILLIPEDE
1.0–1.5 in.
coiled

CENTIPEDES are flat-bodied, with long antennae and one pair of legs on nearly every trunk segment. The House Centipede feeds on ants, flies, cockroaches, and other pests, hence is beneficial. Its bite, though rare, is painful. Use residual contact insecticides or treat joists, subfloors, and cracks with creosote or other repellents.

MILLIPEDES are almost cylindrical, with two pairs of short legs per apparent body segment, and short antennae. They move slowly. These features distinguish them from swift-crawling centipedes. Normally millipedes are found only outdoors, feeding on decaying vegetation, but they may invade houses after rains or to escape cold in fall.

SOWBUG
0.6 in.

coiled

PILLBUG
0.6 in.

SCORPION
2.0–3.0 in.

PILLBUGS AND SOWBUGS are land-dwelling crustaceans. They can survive only in damp places, as in leaf mold or in basements. They feed mainly on decaying vegetation but also eat tender roots of plants. Controls: cleanup of debris in which they thrive; contact insecticides; poison baits in heavy infestations, as in greenhouses.

SCORPIONS are spider relatives found only in warm climates. Two species in southwestern U.S. are highly poisonous. Scorpions are nocturnal and feed mainly on insects, which they catch in their pincers, then paralyze or kill with their sting. Eliminate debris close to buildings and use contact insecticides that have residual action.

young on female's back

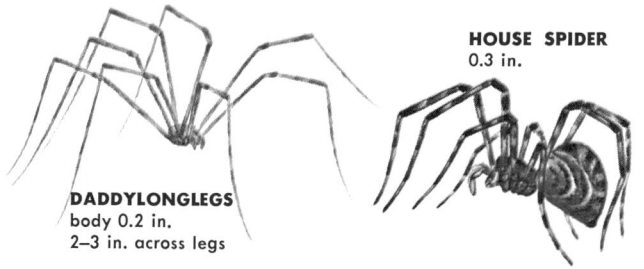

HOUSE SPIDER
0.3 in.

DADDYLONGLEGS
body 0.2 in.
2–3 in. across legs

DADDYLONGLEGS, or Harvestmen, resemble spiders but have a distinctly segmented abdomen and stink glands. They lack silk glands. Their long stiltlike legs are easily shed when the animal is touched. Daddylonglegs are harmless, feeding mainly on dead insects. They will kill and eat small insects, however, and may feed on fruits or vegetables.

JUMPING SPIDERS of several species often enter houses. They do not make webs. Instead they hunt actively for prey, searching over ceilings, walls, sills, and floors. They can jump quickly, and frequently use their silk as a payout line to let themselves down from high levels. These lines may be a nuisance, but the spiders are helpful.

BLACK WIDOW SPIDERS are widely distributed and rather abundant. Their bites are painful and may cause death. A doctor should be called immediately to give treatment. Fortunately, Black Widows are shy and do not bite without great provocation. They usually build their webs in or beneath objects close to the ground.

HOUSE SPIDERS bother housewives because of their webs. Their bites may be very poisonous. House Spiders prey on the House Fly and other insects. Their webs are usually built in corners, where they collect dust as well as prey. These and other spiders can be killed with contact sprays or dusts; residual insecticides prevent reinfestation.

JUMPING SPIDER
0.4 in.

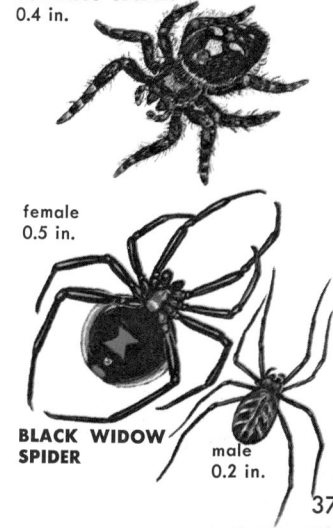

female
0.5 in.

BLACK WIDOW SPIDER

male
0.2 in.

37

Biting flies feed on the blood of their victims. They cut or stab through the skin with their knife-sharp piercing mouthparts, then lap up blood that flows from the wound. They may also be carriers of diseases.

Insects that sting usually do so as a defense when disturbed or annoyed. Stings of bees or wasps may be extremely painful and also dangerous. In the United States more deaths result from insect stings than from the bites of poisonous snakes. Medical knowledge about the effect of insect venoms and how to treat stings is still limited. Usually there is swelling and in many cases a throbbing ache that may last for several days. Stings vary in severity with the species of insect and also with the amount of poison injected. A sting in an arm or a leg is less dangerous than a sting in the neck, where the poison may paralyze the vocal cords or hamper breathing. The effect of a sting also varies with individuals and with their physiological condition. Beekeepers commonly build up an immunity to stings.

HORSE FLIES, active only in the daytime, are mainly pests of livestock (p. 56) but may also bite people. The bite, only from females, is very painful. Females lay egg masses on leaves, stems, or rocks.. On hatching, larvae drop to ground and complete development in damp soil or in water. Maggots may overwinter in mud, pupate in early spring, and emerge as adults a few weeks later. Equally pestering are closely related Deer Flies.

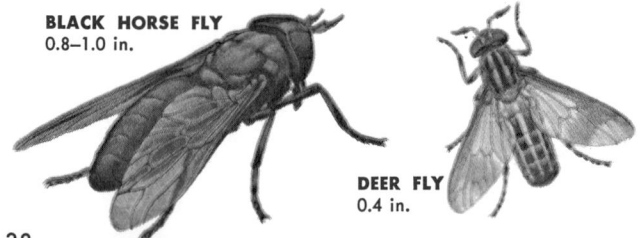

BLACK HORSE FLY
0.8–1.0 in.

DEER FLY
0.4 in.

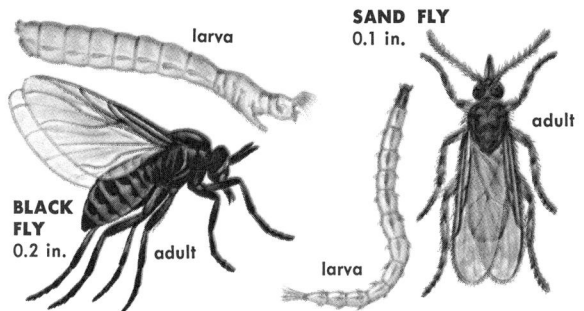

SAND FLY
0.1 in.

adult

larva

BLACK FLY
0.2 in.

adult

larva

BLACK FLIES, also called Buffalo Gnats, are most abundant in late spring and summer in wooded regions of Canada and the U.S. These humpbacked bloodsuckers (only the females bite, causing a persistent irritation) crawl annoyingly into the eyes, ears, and nostrils. Females fasten their egg masses to rocks or vegetation in streams, in which the larvae develop and spin cocoons. A life cycle is completed in about six weeks. Repellents are effective.

STABLE FLIES, like Horse Flies, are principally pests of livestock but may at times bother people. They occur most abundantly in lowlands and seashore areas, becoming especially aggressive when the barometer is falling. Both sexes bite. Their mouthparts are sharp and stiletto-like rather than sponging, as in House Flies. In cool areas, they overwinter as larvae or pupae; in warmer climates, active the year around. In houses, can be killed with sprays. Eliminate breeding places (manure or decaying organic matter).

SAND FLIES, or No-See-Ums, are tiny bloodsucking flies, so small they can go through ordinary screens. They are most active in evening or early morning hours, and their bites are extremely painful. Screens and areas around lights can be sprayed or painted with an oil-emulsion contact insecticide. Repellents will keep the flies off in daytime. The maggots develop in moist vegetation or in pools (some species in salt water, others in fresh).

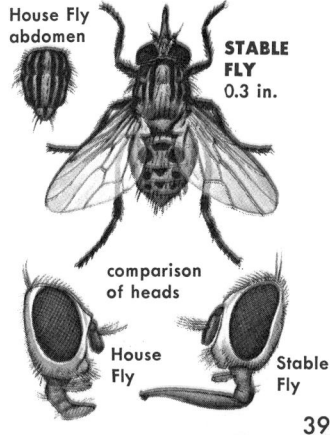

House Fly abdomen

STABLE FLY
0.3 in.

comparison of heads

House Fly

Stable Fly

MOSQUITOES total more than 2,500 species. Many are carriers of diseases (malaria, yellow fever, dengue, and filariasis). Others, as annoyances, cause costly losses of man-hours to outdoor workers or reduce the pleasure of being outdoors.

Adult females lay their eggs on or near the surface of permanent pools or in moist or temporarily flooded locations. Some species lay their eggs singly; others deposit them in "rafts" of as many as several hundred. In most species the female must have a meal of blood before she can produce eggs. Males are nectar feeders and do not bite. The larvae, also called "wigglers," swim or rest just beneath the surface. They feed on microscopic organic matter. Development may be completed in as short a time as five days or may require several months; the average is a week to 10 days. Then the larvae transform into pupae, also known as "tumblers" because they continue to be active. The adults emerge in from two days to two weeks or longer, depending on the species and the water conditions. Adults live for a few days to several months, and most species do not travel more than a mile. Some hibernate in the adult stage.

Large-scale mosquito control consists of eliminating breeding areas by drainage, spreading oil films over the surface of the water, using insecticides to destroy the larvae or pupae, or spraying with contact insecticides to kill the adults. All of these controls may also destroy habitats or kill fish, birds, or other valuable wildlife and should be undertaken only after careful study by professionally trained people. Around houses, get rid of breeding places, such as ditches, low spots where water stands in lawns, or containers. Screening will keep adults out of houses.

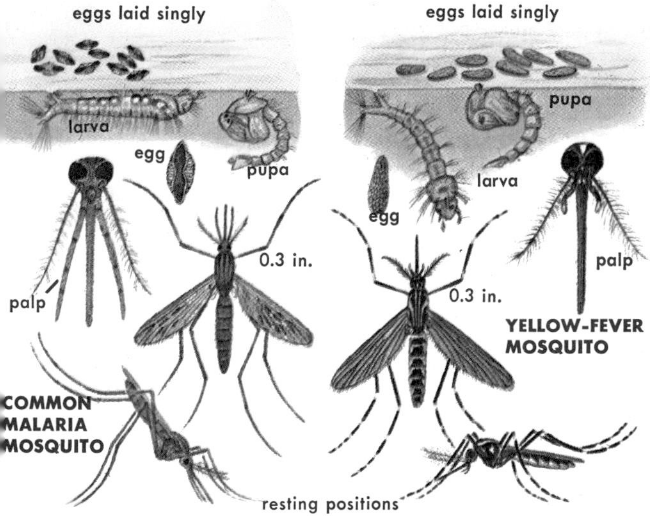

eggs laid singly

eggs laid singly

larva

egg

pupa

pupa

larva

egg

palp

0.3 in.

0.3 in.

palp

YELLOW-FEVER MOSQUITO

COMMON MALARIA MOSQUITO

resting positions

COMMON MALARIA MOSQUITO and the Western Malaria Mosquito, known to migrate 25 miles in spring flights, transmit malaria in N.A.

SALT-MARSH MOSQUITOES breed in large numbers along Atlantic and Gulf coasts. A related black species occurs in South, others in West.

YELLOW-FEVER MOSQUITO, found mainly in port areas in South, is recognized by silvery stripes. Unlike most mosquitoes, it bites during day.

HOUSE MOSQUITO, worldwide in distribution, becomes active and bites at night. Members of this genus carry the virus causing encephalitis.

SALT-MARSH MOSQUITO

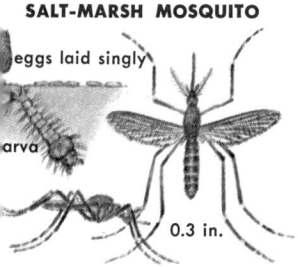

eggs laid singly

larva

0.3 in.

HOUSE MOSQUITO

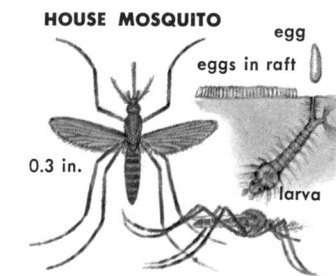

egg

eggs in raft

0.3 in.

larva

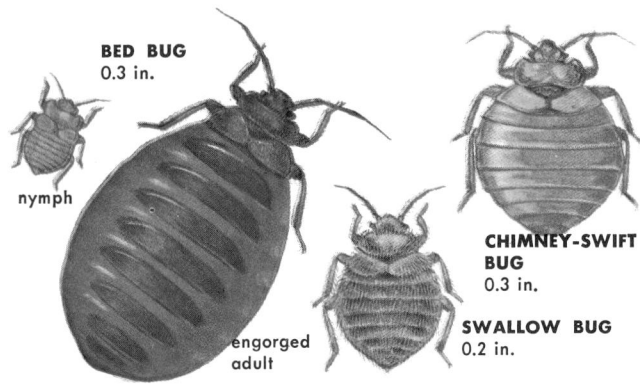

BED BUG
0.3 in.

nymph

engorged
adult

**CHIMNEY-SWIFT
BUG**
0.3 in.

SWALLOW BUG
0.2 in.

BED BUGS feed on the blood of birds and mammals, including man. Both males and females bite, and as a rule, are active only at night. They pierce the skin and inject saliva that later causes the bite to itch or swell, the degree of irritation varying with the sensitivity of the individual. After becoming engorged, in five minutes or less, the bugs crawl away to hide. Bed Bugs breed the year around. Each female lays four to five eggs a day over a period of about two months, gluing them to rugs, furniture, or walls or laying them in cracks or crevices. The nymphs resemble the adults but are pale. After feeding and shedding (five molts), they become adults, living as long as a year. Bed Bugs are transported in bedding, furniture, or clothing. Heavy infestations can be detected by the odorous secretions given off by the bugs. Related species such as the Bat Bug, Chimney-swift Bug and Swallow Bug may also become pests in houses at times. To eliminate, spray floors, furniture, and walls with a residual contact insecticide in oil or water emulsion. Fumigation, necessary if infestations are spreading from chimneys or similar locations, should be done by a professional.

LICE are wingless insects parasitic on a variety of host animals. Those infesting pets, poultry, and livestock are described on pages 52–53. Three types may occur on humans. The Head Louse confines itself almost exclusively to the hair of the head, to which it glues its eggs or nits. The Body Louse, similar to the Head Louse in appearance, hides in clothing when not feeding. It lays its eggs in the clothes, especially in the seams. The Crab Louse, nearly as broad as it is long, lives among the coarse hairs of the body. The stout, curved claws on its first pair of legs do not form a locking device, as do those of the Head Louse and the Body Louse. All three types are bloodsuckers that may become abundant in unsanitary conditions. Their bite is not felt immediately but later becomes an itchy swelling. Lice are carriers of typhus fever and other diseases, transmitted through their bites. Young lice resemble the adults both in appearance and habits. Complete development, from egg to mature adult, takes about a month. Lice can be killed by dusting the clothing and body with a contact insecticide, such as DDT. Clothing can also be washed in an insecticide solution. Living quarters should be fumigated or subjected to a heat of 160 degrees F., steam or dry, for six hours or longer to destroy eggs.

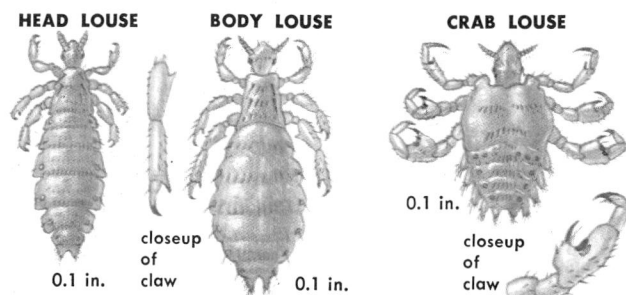

HEAD LOUSE   **BODY LOUSE**   **CRAB LOUSE**

0.1 in.

closeup of claw

0.1 in.

0.1 in.

closeup of claw

ASSASSIN BUGS also go by the name of Conenoses because their head and mouthparts form a conelike beak. These insects bite quickly when disturbed. They should be brushed off swiftly but gently, and no attempt should be made to pick them up. They are bloodsuckers, thrusting their beaks forward to pierce the skin of their victim. The bite of some species is painless; the bite of others is extremely painful, the effects of the venom often lasting for months. Some are carriers of diseases, such as the very dangerous Chagas' disease of the American tropics. Some live in the nests of bats, rats, and other mammals. Where conenoses are abundant, spraying around doorways and lights with a residual contact insecticide will help to control them.

MASKED HUNTERS prey on Bed Bugs and other insects, from which they suck blood. The nymphs are covered with a sticky secretion to which lint and other camouflaging debris adheres to "mask" them. Also known as Kissing Bugs, the adults feed on warmblooded animals and may bite man. Occurs in eastern and midwestern U.S.

BLOODSUCKING CONENOSES, of southern and southwestern United States and Mexico, are known in some areas as Mexican Bed Bugs. At times they become locally abundant and may enter houses. They feed at night. Outdoors the eggs are laid on plants; indoors, in dark, dusty cracks or corners. The nymph stage may last a year or longer.

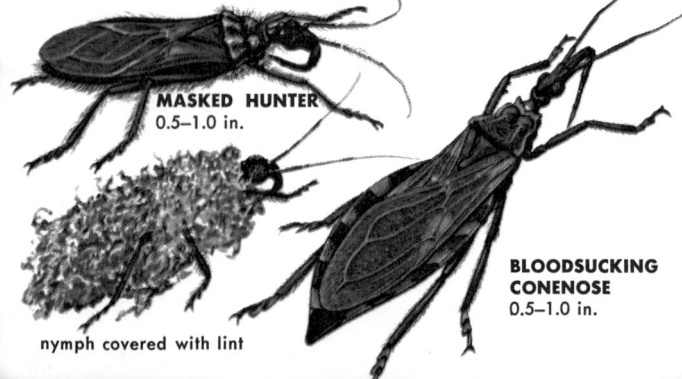

MASKED HUNTER
0.5–1.0 in.

BLOODSUCKING CONENOSE
0.5–1.0 in.

nymph covered with lint

CHIGGERS, also called Jiggers or Red Bugs, are parasitic mites, more closely related to ticks and spiders than to insects. Some of the many species of mites are pests of poultry, pets, and livestock (p. 54). The tiny reddish adult chiggers, just visible to the naked eye, may be seen scurrying about in litter or in soil. The smaller larval stage that attacks man is the first of two stages before the mites become adults. The larvae wait on grass, leaves, or in litter for a victim. They usually crawl until they reach a belt line, an armpit, or similar obstruction, and there stop to feed by inserting their mouthparts into the skin to draw out fluids. When full, they drop off. As they feed, they release into the bite a digestive fluid containing a toxin that liquefies the cells and tissues and later causes swelling and intense itching. Dusting the clothing, particularly the cuffs, sleeves, and neckline areas, with sulfur helps to discourage chiggers, as do insect repellents. Or, before going into grassy or brushy areas, cover your arms and legs with a soapy lather and allow it to dry. Treat lawns infested with chiggers with a residual contact insecticide, and eliminate such breeding spots as weedy patches or plant debris. The chigger bites can only be soothed with ointments.

ITCH MITES spend their entire life on their host. Females burrow into the skin, sometimes making a tunnel an inch long, in which they lay as many as two dozen eggs. Both the tunneling and the feeding cause the itching, or scabies, and the bite spot commonly becomes infected. Ointments prescribed by a doctor will get rid of the mites and relieve the itching. Clothing and bedding should be sterilized.

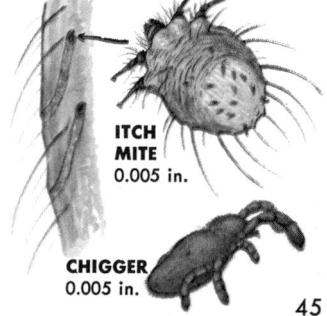

ITCH MITE
0.005 in.

CHIGGER
0.005 in.

TICKS of several species are bloodsucking pests of man and his pets and livestock (p. 48). They are more closely related to spiders than to insects. Some ticks transmit diseases, the most dangerous of which is spotted fever. Bites of some ticks cause paralysis. When a tick is attached, do not try to pull it off, as the head and mouthparts usually break off and are left in the wound. Alcohol or ammonia applied to a tick's posterior will cause most ticks to release. Wait for 15–20 minutes before trying to remove tick. Engorged females drop from their host and lay their eggs on the ground or in debris. The larvae of most species feed on small animals, then become dormant until the following spring. They feed again and in about two months become adults, which in temperate climates do not feed until the next spring. It is at this stage that ticks feed also on man. Insect repellents will help to keep ticks off outdoors. After an outing in a tick-infested area, clothing should be removed and washed. Lawns or gardens can be sprayed with a contact insecticide.

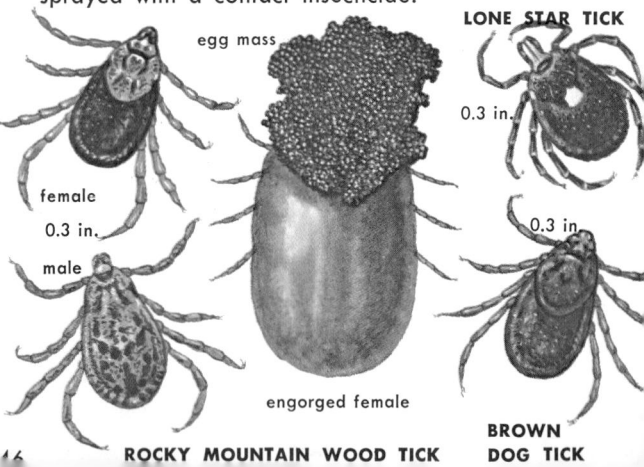

LONE STAR TICK

egg mass

0.3 in.

female

0.3 in.

male

0.3 in.

engorged female

BROWN DOG TICK

ROCKY MOUNTAIN WOOD TICK

PUSS CATERPILLAR 1.0 in.

SADDLEBACK CATERPILLAR 1.0 in.

HAG MOTH CATERPILLAR 1.0 in.

STINGING CATERPILLARS have hollow hairs (setae) connected at their base to cells that secrete a poison. They may be in tufts or scattered over the body. When one of these spinelike hairs contacts the skin, the poison goes into the wound and causes either an itching or a painful swelling. Learn to recognize caterpillars that have stinging hairs and avoid touching them.

WASPS AND BEES have a stinger at the end of their abdomen. It is connected to a poison gland. These insects do not sting unless molested and are most troublesome when they nest in places where disturbing them is unavoidable. The occasional wasp or bee that gets indoors can be let out or killed. Spraying the nest with a residual contact insecticide, either as a dust or in an oil or water emulsion, will get rid of those few that become problems outdoors. It is best to spray at night, when the nest is fully occupied and the insects are not active. Stings can be soothed with ice packs or with a bicarbonate-of-soda paste. If the effects of a sting are severe, a doctor should be consulted promptly.

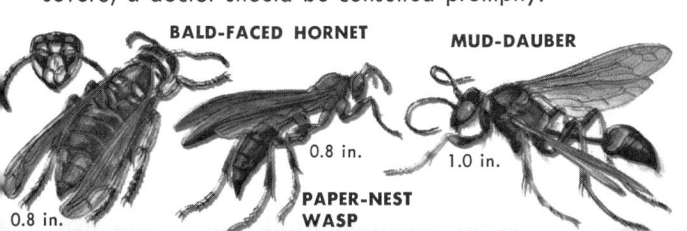

BALD-FACED HORNET

MUD-DAUBER 1.0 in.

0.8 in.

PAPER-NEST WASP

0.8 in.

PESTS OF PETS, POULTRY, AND LIVESTOCK

Insect pests of pets and domestic animals may be carriers of deadly diseases or of parasites that weaken the animals. Some of the diseases may be transmitted to man. Even pests that only bite or cause itching may reduce an animal's productiveness. Also, the animal's resistance to diseases may be lowered.

TICKS are more closely related to spiders than to insects. In addition to being annoyances or in extreme infestations causing anemia, these bloodsuckers carry such diseases as spotted fever and tularemia. The complex life cycle of ticks may require three years or longer. Females, after a blood meal, lay as many as 6,000 eggs, which hatch into tiny six-legged larvae, or seed ticks. Nymphs feed on mice or other small animals, and in most species only the adults attack such large animals as dogs, cats, horses, cattle, or man. Other species are discussed on p. 46.

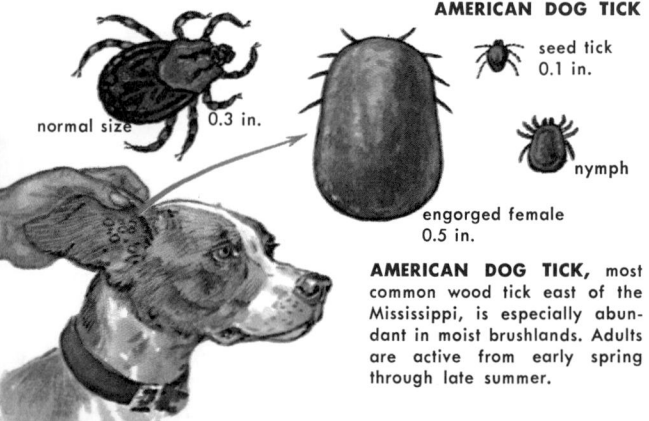

AMERICAN DOG TICK

normal size · 0.3 in.

seed tick 0.1 in.

nymph

engorged female 0.5 in.

AMERICAN DOG TICK, most common wood tick east of the Mississippi, is especially abundant in moist brushlands. Adults are active from early spring through late summer.

CATTLE TICKS of southern U.S., Central and South America, Africa, and parts of Europe transmit tick fever (Texas fever or cattle fever). The disease, spread only by ticks, may be fatal in a high percentage of cases. Tiny one-celled animals passed into the host's bloodstream by the tick destroy red blood corpuscles. Sheep, horses, mules, goats, deer, and other large animals are also susceptible. Cattle ticks winter in pastures in the egg stage or as seed ticks, or they may spend the winter as nymphs or adults on host animals. A rotation use of pasture may starve seed ticks, though they can live for months without feeding. Cattle in tick-infested areas are quarantined, and are dipped (usually forced to swim through vats of insecticide solution) to kill ticks.

EAR TICKS, of southwestern U.S., are parasites only as nymphs, which crawl into the outer ear of sheep, horses, cattle, or other animals to gorge on blood. When full, they drop off and shed to become adults, which do not feed. Heavy infestations may cause deafness. Ear Ticks are killed with insecticides applied to the ear or head.

FOWL TICKS feed only at night, attaching to the bare skin under wings or around head. During the day they hide in cracks or crevices near roost. Worldwide in distribution in warm, dry climates, they transmit poultry diseases. Roosts are sprayed with a residual contact insecticide.

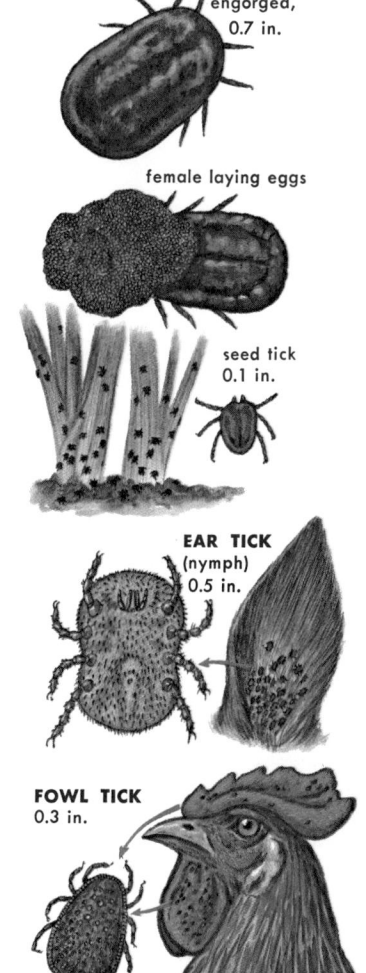

CATTLE TICK
engorged,
0.7 in.

female laying eggs

seed tick
0.1 in.

EAR TICK
(nymph)
0.5 in.

FOWL TICK
0.3 in.

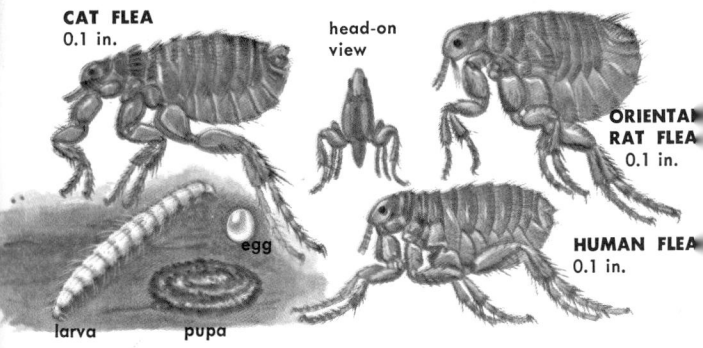

CAT FLEA
0.1 in.

head-on view

ORIENTAL RAT FLEA
0.1 in.

HUMAN FLEA
0.1 in.

egg

larva   pupa

CAT FLEAS and Dog Fleas are similar in appearance and habits. Neither is restricted to the animal for which it is named, and both will bite humans.

HUMAN FLEAS are pests of man but also occur on rats, dogs, cats, and other animals. Like the Oriental Rat Flea, they may be carriers of bubonic plague.

FLEAS are wingless, bloodsucking parasites of pets, livestock, and man. A flea's body is compressed or flattened from side to side, enabling the insect to move with ease between the hairs on an animal's body. Its stiff hairs and spines (setae) project backward. When off its host, a flea travels rapidly by jumping.

An adult female flea lays small, whitish eggs on her host's body or in the host's den or nest. The eggs drop from the hair as the animal moves about or shakes itself and are commonly abundant where the animal sleeps. In about two weeks the eggs hatch into tiny, eyeless, wormlike larvae that feed on the droppings of adult fleas or other organic matter in an animal's bedding, in dust or lint, or in carpeting. Depending on the species, weather, and availability of food, the larvae complete their growth in a few days to six months or longer. When full grown, each spins a silken cocoon in which it pupates for a few days to several months before

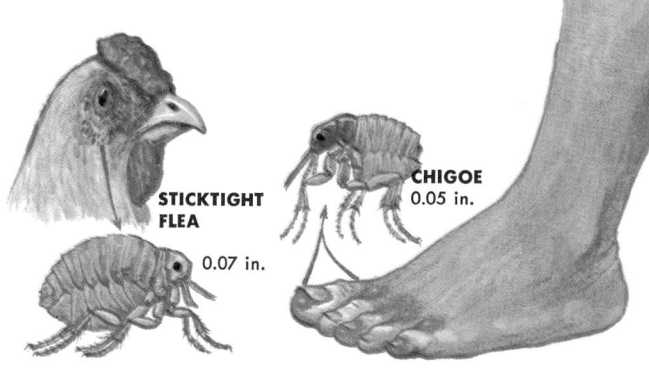

STICKTIGHT FLEA 0.07 in.

CHIGOE 0.05 in.

STICKTIGHT FLEAS, of southern U.S., are flat-bodied and cling like ticks. They cluster on combs or bare skin of poultry, also on dogs, cats, and man.

CHIGOES are tropical fleas, not related to chiggers (p. 45), found rarely in southern U.S. Females burrow under the skin to lay their eggs.

emerging as an adult. Adults can live for long periods without food, especially in cold weather. In warm weather fleas may breed outdoors in dry places.

Fleas have piercing-sucking mouthparts. The painful bites may become swollen or inflamed. Some people or animals are more sensitive to the bites than others are. Before it begins to feed, a flea usually spits out a spot of partly digested blood near the bite. It may also leave wastes. These, with whatever disease organisms they contain, may spread into the bite.

Control of fleas consists of getting the adults off the infested animal by bathing it or dusting it with a contact insecticide. Equally important, the eggs, larvae, and pupae must be destroyed and the places where they develop cleaned and treated with a residual contact insecticide. Cats, because they lick themselves regularly, are especially susceptible to insecticide poisoning. Read labels. Consult a veterinarian if in doubt.

LICE, of which there are several thousand species, are divided into two groups—biting or chewing lice, principally pests of poultry and other birds; and sucking lice, parasites on mammals. Sucking lice feed only on blood, hence may be carriers of disease. Both kinds are wingless and have poorly developed or no eyes. A louse's body is flat, and its claws are developed for clinging. At hatching, young lice look like the adults, but are smaller. Before becoming adults, they molt several times, the number varying with the species. Most lice are confined to a single or to closely related host species. Some occur only on a particular body area. Lice move to a new animal if the host dies, if they become too numerous, or by contact. Those that infest humans are sucking lice (p. 43).

POULTRY LICE feed by chewing on feathers or dried skin, causing discomfort or irritation mostly as a result of their crawling. Louse-infested poultry are poor egg layers and are susceptible to diseases. Their wings droop, and they become drowsy. Young birds may die. The Chicken Head Louse occurs mainly on the head and neck areas, Chicken Body Lice on body feathers. The lice are spread from one bird to another either by direct contact or in heavy infestations by swarming over the roost. Female lice attach eggs (nits) to down feathers with a gluey secretion. The eggs hatch in about 10 days, and the young become adults about 10 days later. Poultry lice can be killed by dusting or spraying with a contact insecticide while birds are on roost. Birds can be treated individually by dipping in an insecticide solution or by dusting.

0.1 in.

nit on down feather

CHICKEN HEAD LOUSE

infested chicken

0.1 in.

CHICKEN BODY LOUSE

SHEEP-BITING LOUSE

0.05 in.

HOG LOUSE

0.3 in.

SHEEP-BITING LICE infest both sheep and goats. Infested animals scratch and rub themselves, often causing sores. The wool on sheep becomes tangled. Contact insecticides applied as wettable powders or dips are the best means of control.

HORSE-BITING LICE chew on skin, dried excretions, or hair, causing an animal great discomfort. Lice are most commonly spread by contact with other infested animals. They are usually most abundant in winter, when an animal's hair is thickest. Treatment in the fall therefore is both a cure and a preventive. Animals should be inspected regularly in winter months and treated again if necessary. Dusts, sprays, or dips are effective, the best method depending on the number of animals to be treated. A related species occurs on cattle. Check with veterinarian about best treatment.

HOG LICE, related to sucking lice that infest cattle, commonly collect about the ears or in folds of skin. They never leave their host except to crawl onto another hog. Control with residual contact insecticides applied as wettable powders or as dips.

SHORT-NOSED CATTLE LICE are bloodsuckers, and heavily infested animals may be weakened from loss of blood. Dairy cattle do not produce as much milk; beef cattle do not put on as much weight. Controls are the same as for Horse-biting Lice, but insecticides that may contaminate milk cannot be used near dairy cattle. Burlap bags treated with an insecticide may be wrapped around a cable and stretched between two posts to give cattle a place to rub themselves and at the same time give themselves a treatment. Check with a veterinarian. A closely related species infests horses.

0.1 in.

HORSE-BITING LOUSE

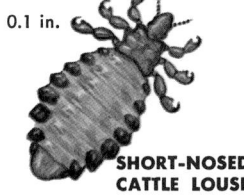

0.1 in.

SHORT-NOSED CATTLE LOUSE

MITES, including ticks, are more closely related to spiders than to insects. Many species are barely visible to the naked eye. Some mites are free-living, others are pests of plants, and some are parasites of animals, including man (p. 45). Itch mites insert their piercing mouthparts into the skin to draw out blood or lymph. As the mites multiply, the feeding areas become larger. Scabs form, and hair or feathers drop out. As they feed, mites also secrete a poison that causes an intense itching. In most species the females burrow into the skin, making a tunnel up to an inch long, in which they lay their eggs and then die. The nymphs shed and become adults in about two weeks. Most mites never leave their host except to crawl onto another animal. Infested animals must be quarantined until cured, and their living quarters must be thoroughly disinfected, as mites are highly contagious and difficult to control. It is best to consult a veterinarian.

ITCH MITES cause an inflamed, scabby skin (mange) on dogs, horses, hogs, cattle, and other animals. The hair drops out as an animal scratches or rubs itself for relief from the itching. Infestations usually start where the skin is tender and hair is thin.

Scab Mites cause so-called "wet mange" (psoroptic scabies) of sheep, cattle, horses, and other animals. They feed on the surface, not burrowing under the skin as Itch Mites do.

Ear Mange Mites live inside the ears of dogs, cats, and wild animals, feeding on the soft skin near the eardrum. The irritation causes the animal to run about wildly, shaking its head. Controlled by swabbing the ears with sweet oil or glycerin.

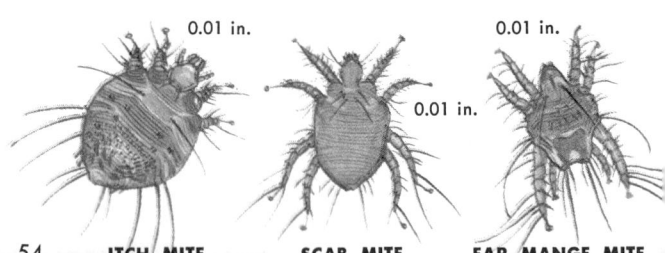

0.01 in.   0.01 in.

0.01 in.

   ITCH MITE   **SCAB MITE**   **EAR MANGE MITE**

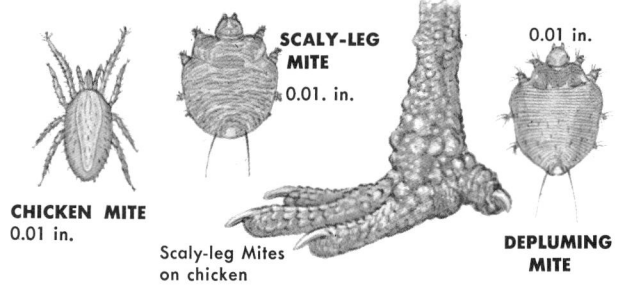

SCALY-LEG MITE
0.01. in.

0.01 in.

CHICKEN MITE
0.01 in.

Scaly-leg Mites
on chicken

DEPLUMING MITE

CHICKEN MITES feed on the blood of chickens or other poultry at night, hiding about the roost during the day. Infested birds become listless and are poor egg layers. Some fowl, particularly the young, are killed. Chicken Mites are most active in spring through summer. Female mites lay their eggs in debris near the roost; nymphs reach the adult stage in about 10 days. Chicken Mites are controlled by treating the poultry house rather than the birds. Clean it thoroughly, then dust, spray, or paint with a residual contact insecticide.

FOLLICLE MITES cause mange of cats, dogs, hogs, cattle, and other animals. The long, worm-like mites burrow deep into hair follicles or into oil glands, commonly around the eyes. Red, pus-filled pimples or nodules form, often becoming infected. To prevent spread of mites in livestock, infected animals are fattened for market and killed. Pens are disinfected thoroughly. Red mange, a serious disease of dogs, is caused by a follicle mite. Consult a veterinarian.

SCALY-LEG MITES stay on the body of their host, like ticks or itch mites, tunneling under the scales of the legs or into the skin of the comb. The scales stand up, and seeping scabs form. In time the infected bird becomes unable to walk. The tiny mites can be killed by soaking the host's legs in soapy water to loosen the scales, then greasing them with oil containing 15 percent sulfur. The Depluming Mite, a related and smaller species, burrows into the skin at the base of the tail feathers. The infected bird pulls out its tail feathers. Use a sulfur dip.

HOG FOLLICLE MITE

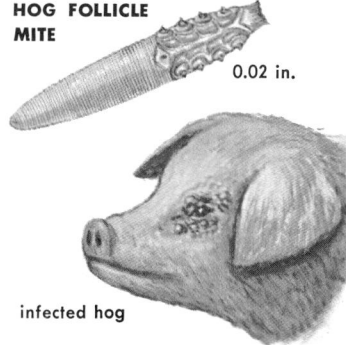

0.02 in.

infected hog

FLIES of some species bite painfully in getting their meal of blood. Those that do not bite worry or annoy animals by getting into their eyes or crawling over their body. Some flies transmit diseases. Many species, including mosquitoes, torment both man and his animals (pp. 32, 39, 40).

HORSE FLIES bite viciously and may also transmit such diseases as anthrax and tularemia. There are more than 100 species in the U.S. (p. 38).

FACE FLIES look like House Flies but are slightly larger. They feed on mucous secretions around the eyes and nostrils of livestock. In some areas they are pests in houses. They lay their eggs in fresh manure, in which the maggots develop and then pupate in the soil nearby. Adults commonly hibernate in the walls of buildings. There is no completely effective control for these pests, which have spread widely throughout the U.S. from Canada since the early 1950's.

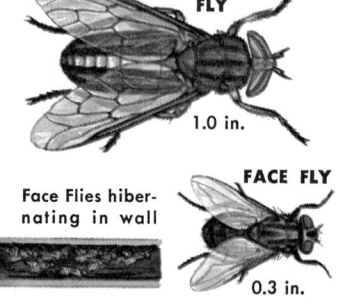

STRIPED HORSE FLY

1.0 in.

Face Flies hibernating in wall

FACE FLY

0.3 in.

HORSE BOT FLIES glue their eggs to the hair of the hind legs or belly of horses or mules, rarely to smaller animals. Each female may lay 500 or more eggs, which hatch in about two weeks, but only if their temperature rises to 100 degrees F. or higher. This will happen if the animal touches them with its tongue. Newly hatched larvae tunnel immediately into membranes of the host's mouth. In about a month they molt and are swallowed. They feed on mucous secretions from the irritated stomach lining to which they fasten themselves. In about 10 months the maggots are full grown and are discharged in wastes. They pupate in the soil and emerge as adults in about three weeks. The Throat Bot Fly lays its eggs on hairs of the neck. The maggots emerge without special stimulation. They crawl to the mouth, often attaching to the pharynx and making it difficult for animal to swallow. Later they enter digestive tract. Eggs of Nose Bot Fly are laid near the lips and will hatch only if kept moist. Lip and throat guards help prevent bot fly infestations. Maggots in digestive tract can be killed with fumigants or with systemic insecticides given by a veterinarian.

SHEEP BOT FLIES occur wherever sheep are raised and may also infest goats or deer. Adult female flies dart rapidly about the sheep, sometimes hovering near the nostrils. Pestered sheep shake their heads, stamp their feet, or run to escape. The female deposits already hatched larvae, or maggots (not eggs), near the sheep's nostrils. She lays only a few at a time but several hundred in her lifetime. Maggots crawl into outer nasal passages, where they feed on mucus. After about two weeks they shed, becoming a size larger, and move deeper into nasal passages. Irritation of membranes by the crawling of spiny-bodied maggots causes a greater flow of mucus, which hinders breathing and may cause death in older or weakened animals. Full-grown maggots (1 in.) crawl out of nasal passage and burrow into soil to pupate, emerging as adults in about a month. In cold climates the small larvae become dormant in outer nasal passages in winter.

Control of Sheep Bot Flies is difficult, especially since it is harmful to kill the grubs in the nasal passages, where their decay will cause an abscess. Small grubs can be killed in the outer passages by irrigation with a 3 percent-Lysol solution. Pine tar applied to the sheep's snout discourages female flies from depositing maggots.

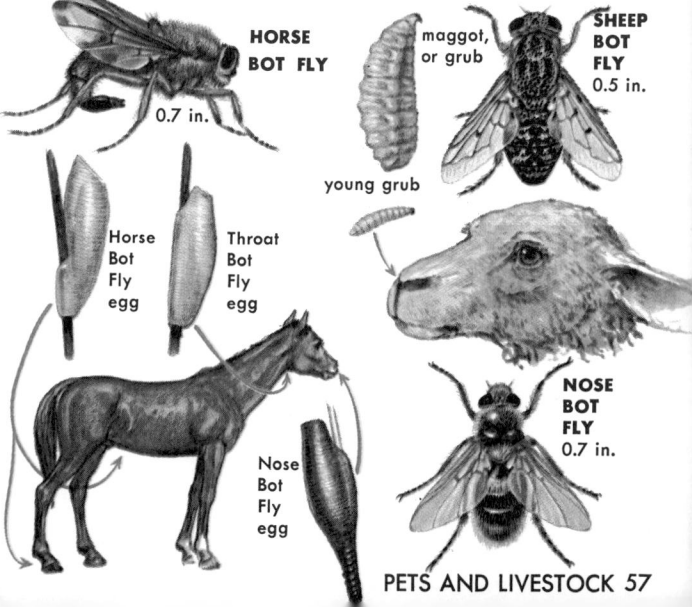

HORSE BOT FLY
0.7 in.

maggot, or grub

SHEEP BOT FLY
0.5 in.

young grub

Horse Bot Fly egg

Throat Bot Fly egg

Nose Bot Fly egg

NOSE BOT FLY
0.7 in.

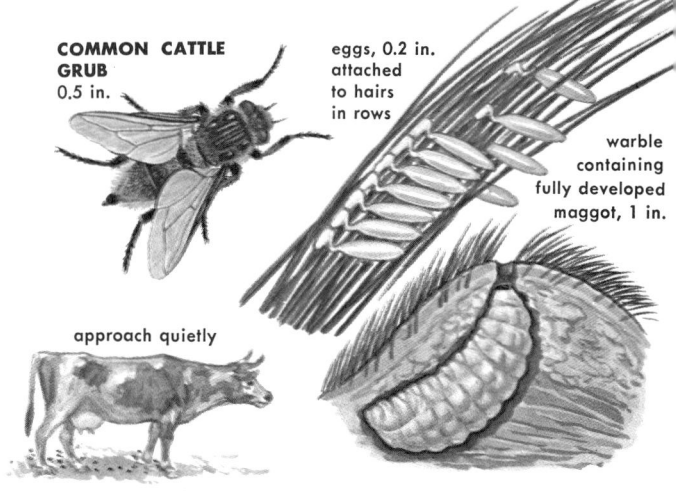

COMMON CATTLE GRUB
0.5 in.

eggs, 0.2 in. attached to hairs in rows

warble containing fully developed maggot, 1 in.

approach quietly

CATTLE GRUBS, or Ox Warbles, are maggots of bot flies. Infestations lower milk production of dairy cattle. The maggots cause a loss of meat in beef cattle, because the flesh must be trimmed around the grubs. Grub holes also reduce value of hides for leather. The Common Cattle Grub (also called Heel Fly) occurs throughout the U.S., the Northern Cattle Grub in Canada and all but southernmost U.S. Female Northern Cattle Grubs approach noisily and lay eggs, one at a time, on the hair of belly or legs. The cattle often stampede to escape bomber-like attacks, though the flies neither bite nor sting. The female Common Cattle Grub, in contrast, approaches victims stealthily, landing on ground nearby and backing up unnoticed to lay her eggs on the heel, or if the animal is lying down, on hair near the ground. She lays many eggs at one visit to her victim.

On hatching, the maggots (wolves) of both burrow into the skin and, over months, migrate through the tissues to the animal's back, where knotlike warbles form. The maggots develop in these cysts during the winter. The swellings are first noticeable in late fall or early winter, becoming large and pus-filled by spring. The spiny maggots feed on mucus that forms in the cysts, and they breathe through a small hole cut in the hide. In spring the maggots squeeze out through the hole and drop to the ground, where they pupate, emerging as adults in two weeks to two months.

Control is most effective if all

NORTHERN CATTLE GRUB
0.5 in.

attack noisily

egg cluster, one to a hair

cattle owners in an area participate in an eradication program, as adult grubs can travel several miles to find victims and start reinfestations. Formerly, cattle grubs could be controlled only in the warble stage, after they had done their damage. This was a safeguard against an increased infestation the next year, however. A 5 percent rotenone dust, sprayed or applied by hand, was used to kill the maggots. The best time for these applications varies with the locality and can be learned by consulting a local agricultural agent. Better controls are possible today with systemic insecticides given orally or applied to the skin. They kill the maggots as soon as they begin to feed on their victim and before they can do damage.

HORN FLIES are common, persistent summertime pests of cattle. Horn Fly bites are painful, as the fly sucks out its meal of blood. Each cow may harbor several thousand flies, which stay with the cow constantly and torment it. Tormented beef cattle lose valuable market weight; dairy cattle give less milk.

Horn Flies lay reddish-brown eggs in fresh manure, on which maggots feed. They pupate in or beneath the dung, a life cycle requiring about 10 days in warm months.

In hot weather the Horn Flies usually rest on an animal's belly or on its shaded side. In cooler weather the flies ride on its back or sometimes on its horns. Horn Flies can be killed by spraying, dusting, or dipping cattle with a residual contact insecticide. Consult a veterinarian or local agricultural agent before applying any insecticide. Avoid especially the use of chlorinated hydrocarbons around dairy cattle, as milk may be contaminated.

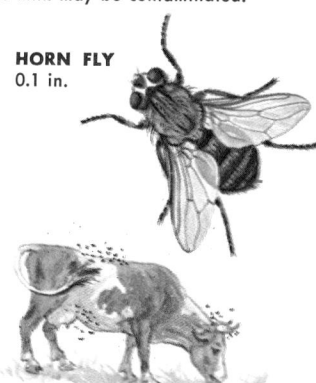

HORN FLY
0.1 in.

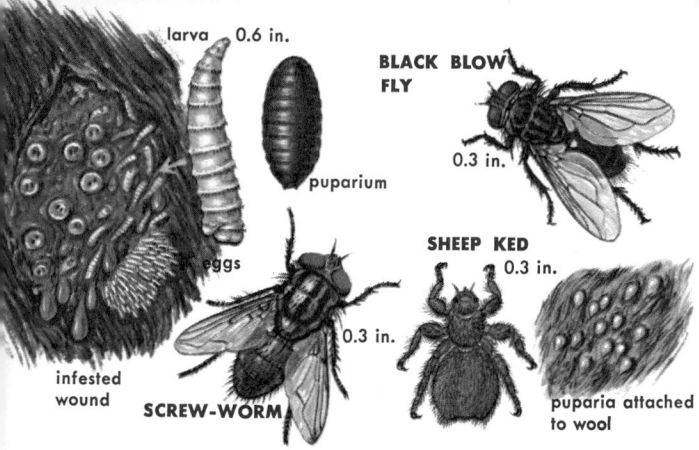

larva 0.6 in.

puparium

BLACK BLOW FLY

0.3 in.

SHEEP KED

0.3 in.

eggs

infested wound

SCREW-WORM

0.3 in.

puparia attached to wool

SCREW-WORMS occur in warm climates, from southern United States southward through the tropics. They infest cattle, swine, sheep, goats, and deer. Females lay clusters of eggs in fresh wounds—such as the bites of the Horn Fly or scratches from thorns or wire—or in the navel of newborn animals. The maggots eat into the flesh, creating a foul-smelling larger wound that attracts Screw-worms or blow flies to lay more eggs in the rotting flesh. If untreated, infested animals will die. Full-grown maggots, with ridges of spines circling the body segments, drop to ground to pupate, completing a life cycle in about 30 days in warm weather. Control of these flies has been successful in Florida and on Curaçao, W.I., by release of millions of sterilized males (p. 23). In other areas animals are treated with an ointment, such as EQ 355, to kill maggots and allow wound to heal.

BLOODSUCKING FLIES of a number of species pester livestock. Included are the Black Blow Fly and the Secondary Screw-worm, which deposit maggots in open wounds. Infestations may become infected. Sprays are effective but use only if prescribed by veterinarian.

SHEEP KEDS are wingless flies commonly thought to be ticks. Adults pierce the skin of their host and suck blood, irritating the animal so that it rubs, bites, or scratches itself and ruins the wool. Sheep Keds spend their entire life on their host. Females give birth to fully developed maggots, gluing them to hair. Within a few hours the larva forms a reddish puparium. Adults emerge in about three weeks. Sheep Keds are found most abundantly on the neck or belly. Infested sheep are sprayed, dipped, or dusted with residual contact insecticides, usually after they have been sheared.

INSECT PESTS OF VEGETABLE CROPS

No vegetable crop is entirely safe from insect pests. Some pest species feed on only one kind of plant; others are general feeders. Some suck the juices from plants; others chew on the roots, leaves, stems, flowers, buds, or fruit. Often a crop is attacked by several pest species at the same time, and in some cases more than one stage in the life cycle of an insect pest is damaging to the same crop.

Some insect pests of vegetable crops can be controlled without the use of chemicals. Crops can be rotated so that pests depending on only one plant species do not build up a large population. Weeds, crop stalks, and other debris in which pests may breed or hibernate can be plowed under. Disking or shallow plowing in winter exposes hibernating stages to freezing temperatures. Some pests can be picked off by hand, or young plants can be covered until large enough to withstand attacks. In many cases crop planting can be timed to miss heavy infestations. Despite these precautions, chemical controls are often the only way now available to protect a crop. Chemicals must be used with great care, for they are dangerous to the person who applies them and also may be absorbed by the vegetable or remain as a poisonous residue.

MOLE CRICKETS, abundant in warm climates, use their stout paddlelike front legs for burrowing. They disturb the roots of young plants and also feed on them. Mole Crickets can be killed with contact insecticides or poison baits applied to the soil before planting.

NORTHERN MOLE CRICKET
1.0 in.

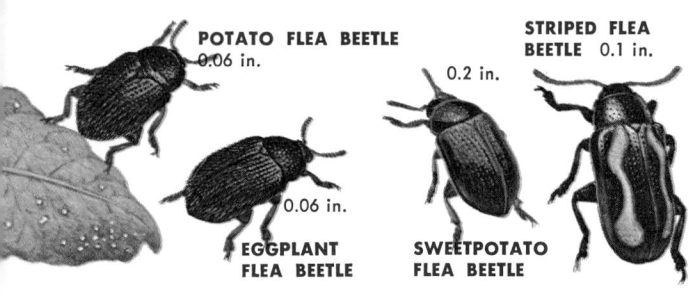

POTATO FLEA BEETLE 0.06 in.

STRIPED FLEA BEETLE 0.1 in.

0.2 in.

0.06 in.

EGGPLANT FLEA BEETLE

SWEETPOTATO FLEA BEETLE

FLEA BEETLES chew small, round holes in leaves, giving a plant the appearance of being peppered with shot. Grubs (larvae) of some species feed on leaves or stems, others on the roots. The many species of flea beetles (so called because of their enlarged hind legs for jumping) feed on a variety of plants, but many, as indicated by the specific names, occur on only one kind or on closely related plants. Most species overwinter as adults beneath debris and thus get an early start in spring. Flea beetles are especially damaging to seedlings, and the holes they eat in the foliage are entry avenues for diseases. Usually there are two generations a year.

Eliminate places where the beetles can hibernate by plowing under weeds or plant stalks. Infested plants can be dusted or sprayed with contact or stomach-poison insecticides to kill adult or immature stages. Do not use insecticides immediately before an edible crop is ready for harvest because of poisonous residues. Follow directions carefully.

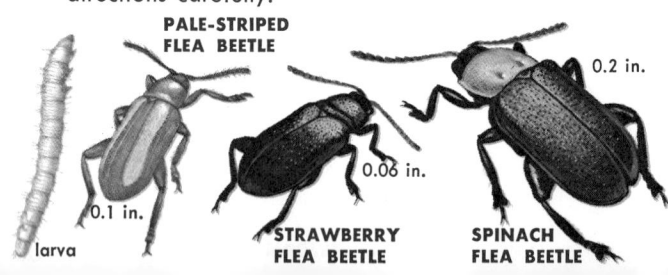

PALE-STRIPED FLEA BEETLE

0.2 in.

0.06 in.

0.1 in.

larva

STRAWBERRY FLEA BEETLE

SPINACH FLEA BEETLE

WIREWORMS are the grubs, or larvae, of click beetles. Those of pest species feed on the underground stems, roots, or tubers of such plants as carrots, beets, potatoes, onions, turnips, beans, and corn. Wireworms may be especially abundant in land recently in grass, though some species live exclusively in cultivated land. Adult female beetles lay their eggs in the soil, and the larvae (wireworms) migrate vertically in the soil, staying at the level where the temperature and moisture are most comfortable for them. Some species become full grown in two years; others do not mature for as long as six years. They change into pupae in the soil. A few weeks later they become adults but do not emerge until following spring. Cultivation from midsummer until freezing weather destroys many larvae and pupae. Infested soil can be fumigated, which kills the worms but gives no lasting protection, or treated with a contact insecticide. Insecticides absorbed by root crops may cause objectionable odors or leave poisonous residues. Check for best method in your area.

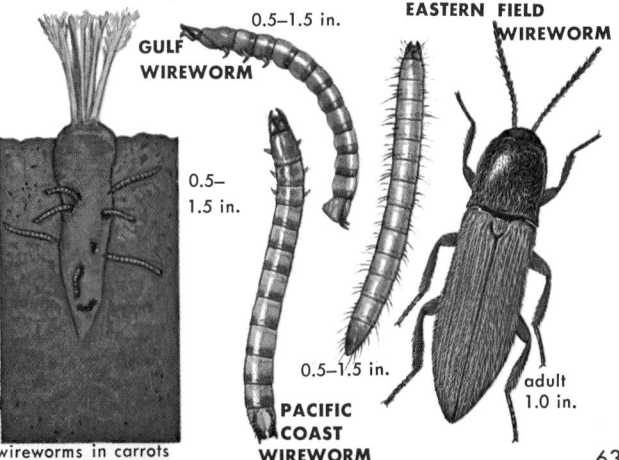

GULF WIREWORM — 0.5–1.5 in.

0.5–1.5 in.

PACIFIC COAST WIREWORM — 0.5–1.5 in.

EASTERN FIELD WIREWORM — adult 1.0 in.

wireworms in carrots

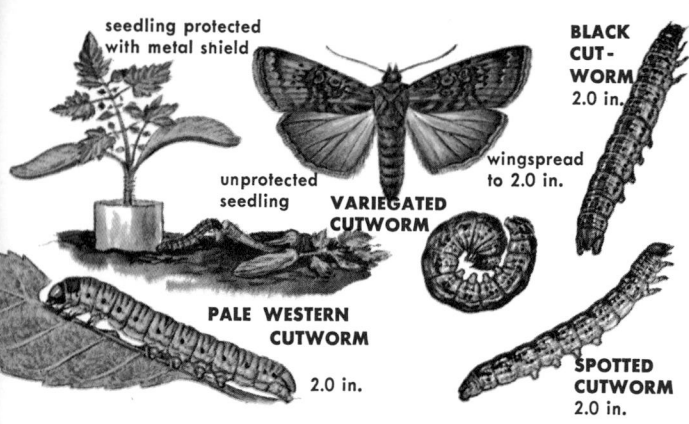

seedling protected with metal shield

unprotected seedling

VARIEGATED CUTWORM

wingspread to 2.0 in.

BLACK CUT- WORM 2.0 in.

PALE WESTERN CUTWORM

2.0 in.

SPOTTED CUTWORM 2.0 in.

CUTWORMS are the fat larvae of a large family of dull-colored, medium-sized moths. More than two dozen species are pests of field and garden crops. Cutworms are classified by their method of feeding—whether underground, at the surface, or above the ground. The most damaging to vegetable crops are species that cut off plants at the surface. Cutworms feed mainly at night. During the day they rest in the soil, coiled in a ball. When full grown, they burrow deeper to pupate. They may emerge as adults in a few weeks or may overwinter as pupae. In warm climates cutworms have several generations a year. Collars of tin cans with the ends removed or of stiff cardboard inserted at least an inch into the soil and sticking above the surface about two inches will protect young plants. Deep plowing or spading in late summer or fall destroys eggs and also exposes the pupae. Poison baits used for grasshoppers (p. 99) are also useful. The soil can be treated with contact insecticides such as chlordane or DDT, but use precautions as noted for Flea Beetles and Wireworms (pp. 62–63) when applying to edible crops.

WHITE GRUBS, the larvae of several species of beetles known as May Beetles or June Bugs, are widely distributed in the U.S. but are most abundant in the Midwest and South. Adult beetles feed on the foliage of trees and are commonly attracted to lights. Females lay their eggs on the ground, commonly in grassy areas. The grubs feed on roots, burrowing deeper into the soil in winter and remaining dormant until spring. Depending on the species, a second, third, or even a fourth summer may be spent as grubs before they pupate. They transform into adults in the fall but do not emerge until spring. Soil infested with white grubs can be treated with a contact insecticide before a crop is planted. In late summer or fall, soil can be turned to expose grubs and pupae to weather and predators.

ASIATIC GARDEN BEETLES are introduced pests that feed on a great variety of plants, including many garden vegetables. First found in 1922 in New Jersey, they have since spread north in coastal states as far as Massachusetts and south to the Carolinas. Apparently they survive only where there is heavy summer rainfall. Asiatic Garden Beetles winter as grubs in the soil, burrowing 8 to 10 inches deep. In spring they move back to the surface to feed on roots, then pupate in late spring or summer. Adults, which look like small, hairy May Beetles, appear in midsummer and feed on foliage until frost. Females usually lay their eggs in grassy or weedy soil. Soil or plants infested with adults or grubs can be treated with a contact insecticide. Adults are attracted to light traps.

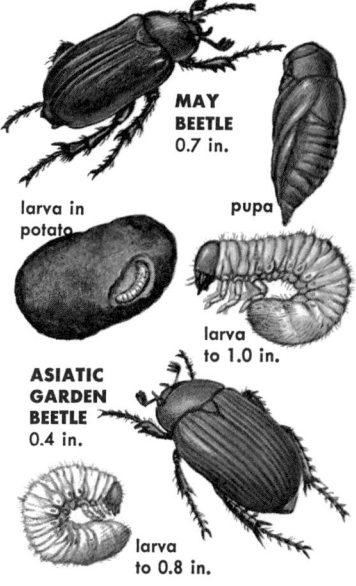

MAY BEETLE 0.7 in.

pupa

larva in potato

larva to 1.0 in.

ASIATIC GARDEN BEETLE 0.4 in.

larva to 0.8 in.

APHIDS, OR PLANT LICE, are small (average 0.2 in.), soft-bodied insects that feed on plants by sucking their fluids or sap. They pierce stems, leaves, buds, roots, and fruit with the slim, needle-sharp stylets in their beak. In abundance, aphids may cause leaves to curl or may stunt a plant's growth and stall its production of flowers or fruit. Eventually the plant may die. Aphids also introduce fungus, bacterial, and virus diseases that can be as damaging as the aphids.

Aphids expel from the end of their abdomen a sticky, sweet substance called honeydew, a favorite food of some species of ants. These ants move the aphids to productive plants and take them into their nests below ground to protect them at night or when the weather is bad (p. 100). Black molds grow on honeydew that drops to the ground beneath plants where aphids are feeding.

In the typical life cycle of aphids that live in temperate climates, winter is passed in the egg stage, glued to the stem or to other parts of plants. Nymphs that hatch from the eggs the following spring grow rapidly to become wingless adults, called stem mothers. Stem mothers give birth to their young, holding the eggs inside their body until they hatch. Within about a week these aphids produce young in a similar manner. More than a dozen generations appear in a short time, forming a feeding cluster on the plant. At intervals some or all of the young develop wings and migrate to other plants, starting new colonies. In some species the winged stages settle on plants of the same kind; in others they always settle on different kinds of plants. In autumn males and females are produced, and the females lay fertilized eggs that overwinter. In warm climates reproduction is continuous.

Aphids are eaten by birds, preyed on by various lady

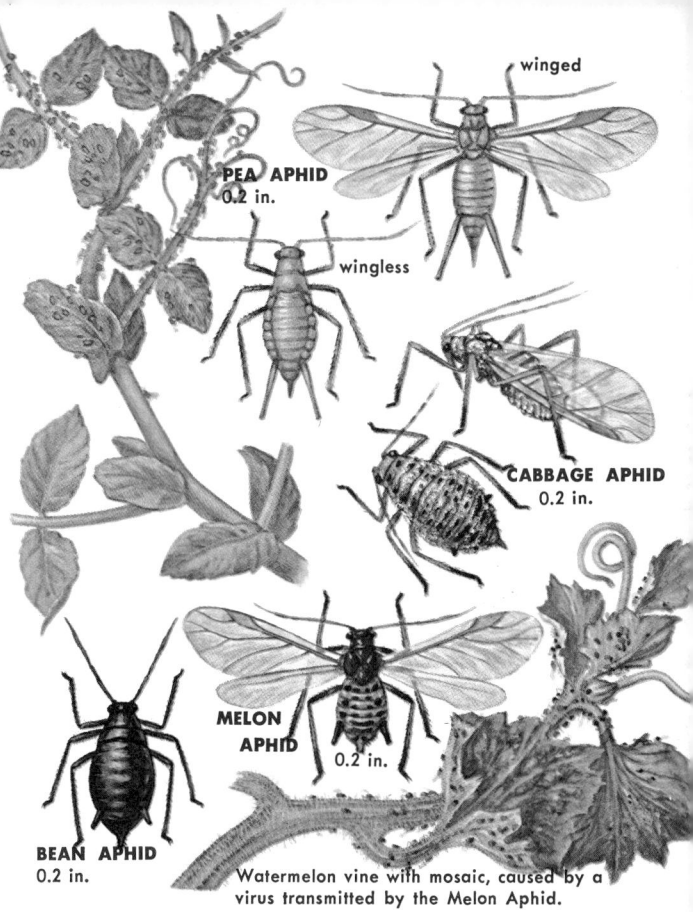

PEA APHID
0.2 in.

winged

wingless

CABBAGE APHID
0.2 in.

MELON APHID
0.2 in.

BEAN APHID
0.2 in.

Watermelon vine with mosaic, caused by a virus transmitted by the Melon Aphid.

beetles, and parasitized by wasps. Chemical controls may be necessary, however, to protect crops when aphids are abundant. Contact insecticides applied as dusts or sprays are effective. Precautions regarding the use of these poisons should be followed, as noted on labels or advised by agricultural agents.

LEAFHOPPERS are small, active insects that damage plants by sucking sap from their leaves. The leaves curl, due either to the loss of sap or possibly to a toxin introduced by the leafhoppers as they feed. Some leafhoppers also spread virus diseases. When disturbed, adult leafhoppers hop into the air and fly away, their wings appearing white in flight. The wingless nymphs run sideways to dodge out of sight on the opposite side of a leaf. Like aphids, leafhoppers excrete from the end of their abdomen a sticky, sweet substance called honeydew. A population of several million leafhoppers may build up on plants on an acre of land in favorable conditions. Contact insecticides sprayed or dusted on the plants will kill the leafhoppers, but the insecticide must reach insects feeding on the underside of the leaves. Do not use insecticides after edible parts of plant have formed, because poisonous residues may remain. Local county agent can give information on best times and the proper dosages of insecticides. To guard against the spread of a virus disease by these pests, it may be necessary to control the leafhoppers on their wintering plants.

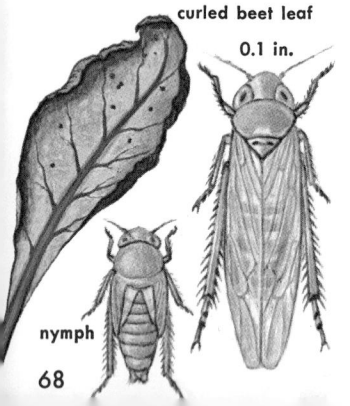

curled beet leaf

0.1 in.

nymph

BEET LEAFHOPPERS are pests in western U.S., ranging east to Illinois. They transmit the virus causing curly top, a disease of sugar beets, beans, spinach, peppers, squash, and other vegetables. Adults winter on wild plants, and in early spring females lay eggs in stems or on the leaves. This generation feeds and matures on wild plants. The second generation invades cultivated crops. As many as five generations may be produced in a season.

POTATO LEAFHOPPERS are damaging pests of potatoes east of the Rocky Mountains. They winter in southern states, migrating as far northward as Canada in spring and summer. Potato Leafhoppers commonly attack young bean plants before appearing on potatoes, because young bean plants apparently contain a greater amount of sugar than do the young potato plants. Females lay their eggs in the stems of leaves, depositing two to three eggs a day over three to four weeks. The nymphs hatch in 10 days and are full grown in about two weeks. Tipburn, or hopperburn, is caused by the feeding of Potato Leafhoppers. First a triangular brown spot appears on a leaf tip; then similar spots show elsewhere, always at end of veins. Eventually entire leaf turns brown and curls.

SIX-SPOTTED LEAFHOPPERS transmit the virus disease called aster yellows. In diseased plants, the young leaves turn yellow, and older leaves become curled and reddish. Lettuce, celery, tomatoes, onions, and carrots are common vegetable crops injured by aster yellows. The Six-spotted Leafhopper winters on weeds or flowers, spreading in spring.

SOUTHERN GARDEN LEAF-HOPPERS, similar and closely related to the Potato Leafhopper, range as far north as New York, though they are most abundant in southern states. They infest ornamentals as well as vegetable crops.

potato leaf with tipburn

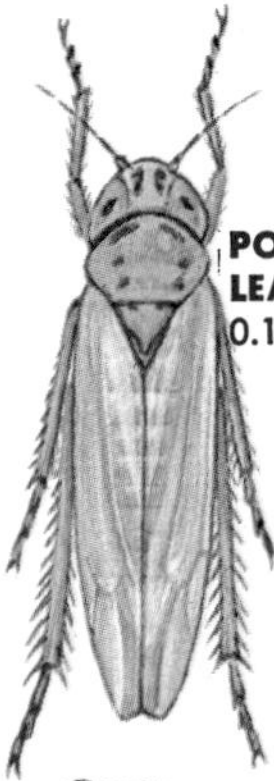

POTATO LEAFHOPPER 0.1 in.

nymph

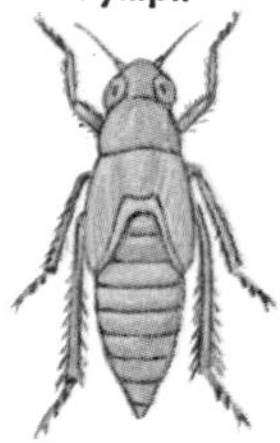

lettuce with aster yellows

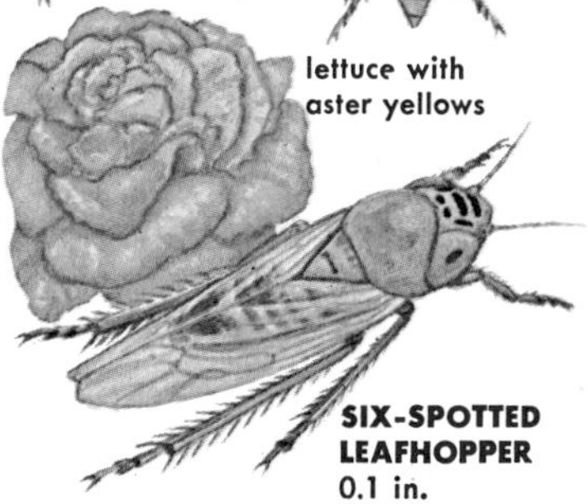

SIX-SPOTTED LEAFHOPPER 0.1 in.

SOUTHERN GARDEN LEAFHOPPER 0.1 in.

sweet potato leaf

69

HARLEQUIN BUG
0.5 in.

eggs

HARLEQUIN BUGS are pests of cabbage, turnips, radishes, and related plants. They have spread from Mexico through most of the U.S. Females lay barrel-shaped eggs on the underside of early planted crops. Nymphs, which hatch in about a week, may kill young plants by sucking out sap. In the South they breed year around; in the North adults hibernate under vegetation.

STINK BUGS do damage, both as adults and as nymphs, by sucking sap from plants and causing them to wilt. Peas, beans, or fruit on which stink bugs have fed become pimpled or malformed. The bugs also give off a strong odor that may be detected on edible parts of plants over which they have crawled. The wingless nymphs generally resemble the adults, though in some species they differ in color. In both, the triangular area, or scutellum, is large and conspicuous. Infested plants can be sprayed with contact insecticides, but this should not be done after edible parts are formed. The bugs are large enough to be picked off by hand.

GREEN STINK BUGS commonly feed on beans, causing pods to fall before they are fully formed. In the South they are also pests of cotton.

SOUTHERN GREEN STINK BUGS are most abundant in southeastern U.S. They feed on most legume crops and on many garden vegetables.

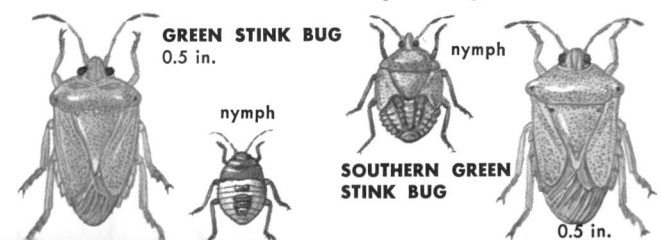

GREEN STINK BUG
0.5 in.

nymph

nymph

SOUTHERN GREEN STINK BUG

0.5 in.

TARNISHED PLANT BUGS feed on more than 50 species of cultivated plants, including beets, celery, and other garden vegetables. A toxin injected into the plant as the bug sucks out its sap deforms the leaves, stems, or fruit. Both adults and nymphs can be killed with contact-insecticide sprays or dusts, but do not use poisonous insecticides after the plant begins to form edible parts. In temperate climates, where the adults hibernate in winter, weeds or similar hiding places should be destroyed.

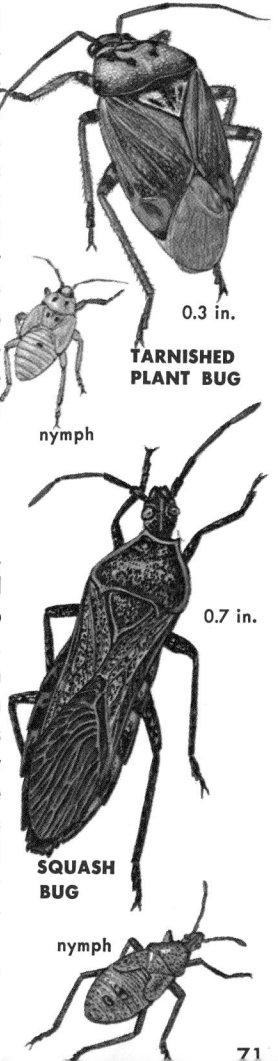

0.3 in.

TARNISHED PLANT BUG

nymph

SQUASH BUGS injure pumpkins, cucumbers, squash, and related plants, first causing the leaves to wilt and then the vine to turn black. Crushed Squash Bugs give off an odor similar to a stink bug's. Squash Bugs are difficult to control, as squash plants are burned by many contact insecticides. Adults can be picked off plants by hand. Leaves that show egg-laying scars should also be removed. Adults may congregate under boards placed between crop rows. In the fall, get rid of all debris under which adults may hibernate.

0.7 in.

SQUASH BUG

nymph

LACE BUGS have a broad thorax and transparent wings with an attractive lacelike pattern. Lace Bugs are known to carry a virus disease of sugar beets, and their feeding in large numbers stunts a plant's growth. Contact insecticides are an effective control.

EGGPLANT LACE BUG
0.1 in.

THRIPS are slender insects with stout, cone-shaped mouthparts. They rasp or scrape the stem or leaf of a plant, then suck out the sap that flows into the wound. If an infestation is heavy a plant's growth is slowed; edible parts of vegetables are poorly formed. Thrips are known also to transmit a virus causing wilt. Most thrips' legs end in a bladder-like swelling that helps them in crawling over smooth surfaces. Most species of thrips have narrow, bristle-like fringed wings. Nymphs are wingless. Of the several thousand species, only a few are pests of specific plants.

ONION THRIPS
0.04 in.

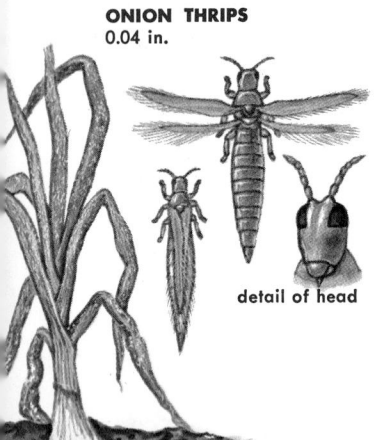

detail of head

ONION THRIPS are especially injurious to onions but feed also on carrots, beans, peas, and other vegetable crops. In winter they hibernate but begin feeding on young plants in early spring, producing a new generation approximately every two weeks in warm weather. Onion leaves turn pale to white, a condition known as silver top. Well-cultivated crops may grow faster than the thrips can do damage. In the fall, bury debris under which thrips might hibernate. Contact insecticides will kill thrips, but they crawl deep into leaves and are hard to reach.

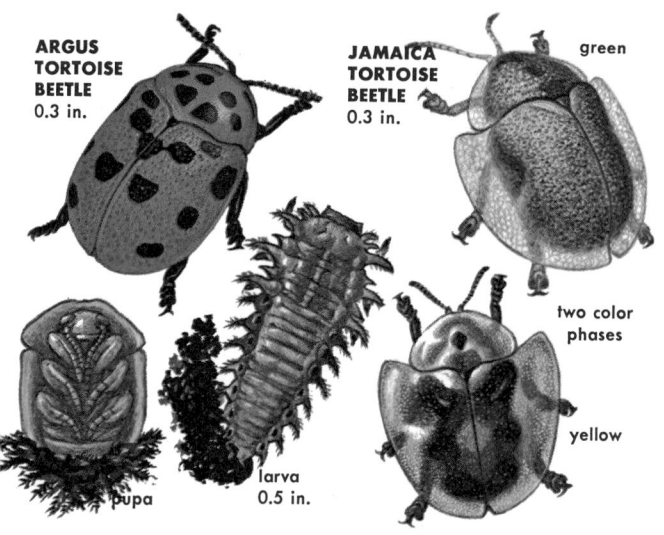

ARGUS TORTOISE BEETLE
0.3 in.

JAMAICA TORTOISE BEETLE
0.3 in.

green

two color phases

yellow

pupa

larva
0.5 in.

TORTOISE BEETLES often go by the name of Gold Bugs because of their metallic colors. Adult beetles hibernate under leaves or other debris on the ground. They emerge in late spring, and the females lay eggs on the stems or underside of leaves of sweet potatoes and other plants of the morning-glory family. The larvae are spiny and covered with a dirty-looking mass consisting of their shed skins mixed with silk and excrement. They feed on the underside of leaves and do the greatest injury to young plants. When full grown the larvae (sometimes called peddlers) form spiny pupae attached to the underside of a leaf. The adult beetle emerges in about a week. Both adults and larvae can be killed with either stomach-poison or contact insecticides applied as dusts or sprays. Cleaning up vines in the fall destroys the hibernating place of the adults.

COLORADO POTATO BEETLES are pests principally of potatoes but also attack tomatoes, peppers, and other garden vegetables. They occur throughout the United States and in Europe, having spread in the 1800's from a limited range on the lower slopes of the Rockies. There they fed on the buffalo or sand bur, a plant related to the potato. Adults emerge from hibernation in early spring and begin feeding on young plants. The females lay their eggs on the lower surface of the leaves. The larvae feed on foliage for two to three weeks, then pupate in soil. Adults emerge in about two weeks and start cycle again. Two generations in a season are usual; sometimes there are three. Both adults and larvae (grubs or slugs) can be picked off by hand, or plants can be sprayed or dusted with a contact or stomach-poison insecticide. Start treatment as soon as beetles appear.

BLISTER BEETLES, or Old-fashioned Potato Bugs, eat the foliage of potatoes, beans, peas, and other vegetables. Only the adults are damaging. Females lay their eggs in the soil, and the burrowing larvae feed on grasshopper eggs. With each of its four molts the larva's legs and mouthparts become smaller compared to the remainder of its body. Winter is passed in an inactive pseudopupa stage. Most species molt the following spring, and the larva becomes active for a short time before entering the true pupa stage. Adults emerge in midsummer. Blister beetles can be brushed into pans of kerosene. Do not touch the beetles with bare hands, as they give off a blistering secretion. The beetles can also be herded along crop rows and trapped in steep-sided ditches. Can be killed with stomach-poison or contact insecticides (except arsenic compounds).

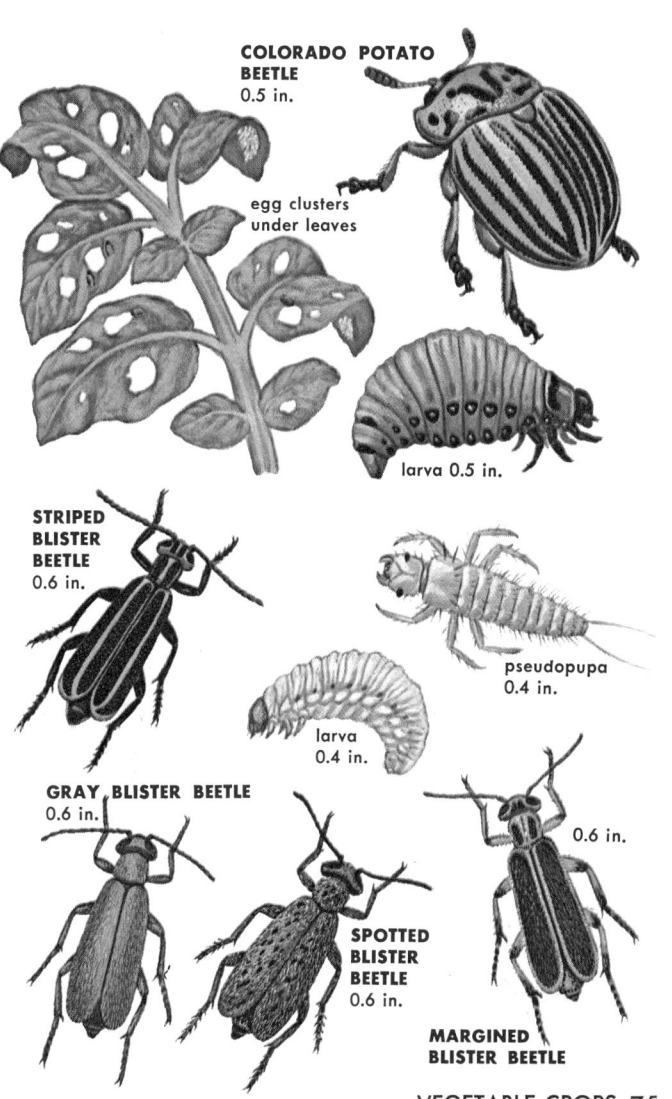

COLORADO POTATO BEETLE
0.5 in.

egg clusters under leaves

larva 0.5 in.

STRIPED BLISTER BEETLE
0.6 in.

pseudopupa
0.4 in.

larva
0.4 in.

GRAY BLISTER BEETLE
0.6 in.

SPOTTED BLISTER BEETLE
0.6 in.

0.6 in.

MARGINED BLISTER BEETLE

MEXICAN BEAN BEETLES and their larvae feed on the foliage of bean plants, eating away the lower surface and leaving only a skeleton of a leaf. When the beetles are abundant, they feed also on bean pods and stems. Native to southwestern U.S. and Mexico, the beetle has spread throughout the U.S., except along Pacific coast. Adult beetles hibernate beneath vegetation and begin feeding in early spring. The eggs, laid on the underside of bean leaves, hatch in about two weeks. When full grown, about a month later, the larvae fasten themselves to the underside of a leaf, shed, and become pupae. Adults emerge in about two weeks and start a second cycle. Three or four generations are common in warm climates. Insecticide sprays or dusts such as rotenone are applied to underside of leaves where insects feed. After beans are harvested, plants should be buried or burned.

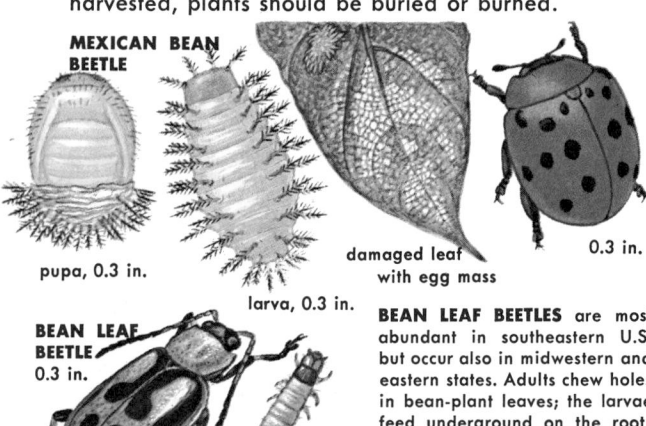

MEXICAN BEAN BEETLE

pupa, 0.3 in.

larva, 0.3 in.

damaged leaf with egg mass

0.3 in.

BEAN LEAF BEETLE
0.3 in.

larva
0.5 in.

BEAN LEAF BEETLES are most abundant in southeastern U.S. but occur also in midwestern and eastern states. Adults chew holes in bean-plant leaves; the larvae feed underground on the roots or on the stems at the soil line. Bean Leaf Beetles can be controlled by the methods used for the Mexican Bean Beetle.

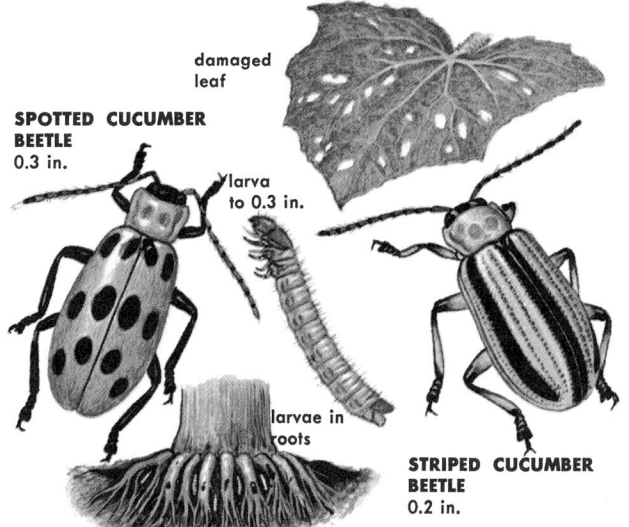

damaged leaf

SPOTTED CUCUMBER BEETLE
0.3 in.

larva
to 0.3 in.

larvae in roots

STRIPED CUCUMBER BEETLE
0.2 in.

CUCUMBER BEETLES, both Spotted and Striped, are general feeders as adults. They chew holes in the foliage and eat on the stems. Adult beetles come out of hibernation in early spring, and females lay their eggs in the soil at the base of plants. These hatch into the worm-like larvae which bore into the roots, where they feed and become mature by midsummer. Spotted Cucumber Beetles are also known as Southern Corn Rootworms, as the larvae bore out young corn plants, and cause them to break off. Larvae of the Striped Cucumber Beetle feed only on the roots of plants in the cucumber or melon family. Adults of both species transmit virus and bacterial diseases. To prevent damage to corn, spring plowing and late planting are recommended, or treat soil with insecticides before planting. Adults can be killed by methods used for Mexican Bean Beetle. Do not use sulfur compounds on cucumber or melon vines.

WEEVILS are a large family of beetles with long, usually down-curved snouts that may in some species be as long as the beetle's body. The snout, an elongation of the head, has the beetle's small chewing mouthparts at its tip; the antennae are located along its sides. The snout is used to puncture leaves, stems, or fruit, for feeding beneath the surface, and also to make holes in which the eggs are laid.

0.4 in.

larvae in turnip

VEGETABLE WEEVIL

VEGETABLE WEEVILS are dormant in summer but become active in fall. Grubs feed at night on many vegetables. Do not spray vegetables to be eaten.

PEPPER WEEVILS, from Mexico, feed inside the buds or in the peppers, causing them to drop off. Several generations may be produced every year.

PEPPER WEEVIL
0.2 in.

pepper with larvae at core

SWEETPOTATO WEEVIL
0.2 in.

larva

larvae in sweet potato

SWEETPOTATO WEEVILS are pests only in the Gulf states. Adults lay their eggs singly in holes on the stems or in the sweet potatoes, and for 2 or 3 weeks the grubs feed and grow either in the vines or in the potatoes. They become pupae in the cavity hollowed by their feeding and emerge as adults in about a week. The adults also feed on the leaves and stems of the sweet potato vine. Pulling dirt high around vines helps to prevent weevils from reaching the potatoes. Plants can be treated with a contact insecticide before planting. After an infestation, burn vines and destroy all infested sweet potatoes. Do not replant sweet potatoes in same field or within one mile of infestation for a year.

WHITE-FRINGED BEETLES, from South America, are general garden pests of southeastern U.S. Adults appear from May through August and feed sparingly. The females reproduce without mating and lay their eggs in sticky masses of 50 or more on rocks, sticks, or stems. The larvae burrow into the soil, where they feed on roots or underground stems. They winter as grubs, forming pupae in the spring. Adults cannot fly (hard outer wings are fused) and can be trapped in steep-sided ditches. Treat soil with a contact insecticide to kill grubs or adults as they emerge.

CARROT WEEVILS damage carrots, celery, parsnips, and related plants. The grubs cut irregular furrows in the roots or may tunnel inside the roots or stems. In winter adults hibernate beneath debris and lay their eggs in early spring. Two and sometimes three generations are produced every season. Early spraying of plants with insecticide will kill adults. Because they feed inside roots or stems, grubs are difficult to kill.

STRAWBERRY ROOT WEEVILS are widely distributed in the U.S. and Europe. In the grub stage they feed on the roots and crown of strawberry plants, which become stunted or die. Adult weevils often hibernate in the crown of the plant; the larvae burrow deep into the soil. Rotate plants to new beds regularly to prevent pest buildup.

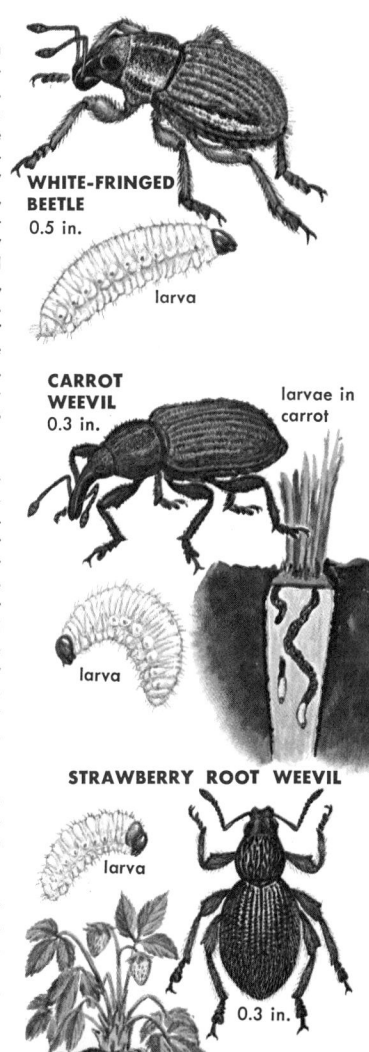

WHITE-FRINGED BEETLE
0.5 in.
larva

CARROT WEEVIL
0.3 in.
larvae in carrot
larva

STRAWBERRY ROOT WEEVIL
larva
0.3 in.

CATERPILLARS, the larvae of butterflies and moths, feed on leaves, stems, flowers, or fruit. Some species tunnel inside, but most species eat from the outside. Large caterpillars can be picked by hand and destroyed. Fall cleanup of debris and turning the soil to expose wintering stages are effective. Among natural controls are wasps that lay eggs on the caterpillars, which become food for wasp larvae. Both stomach-poison and contact insecticides are effective controls.

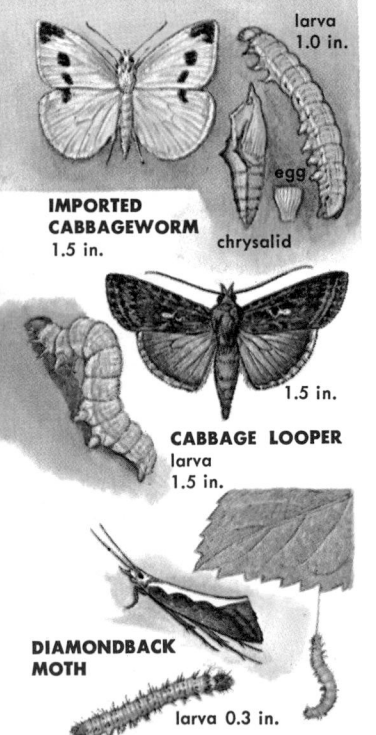

larva 1.0 in.

egg

IMPORTED CABBAGEWORM 1.5 in.

chrysalid

CABBAGE LOOPER larva 1.5 in.

1.5 in.

DIAMONDBACK MOTH

larva 0.3 in.

IMPORTED CABBAGEWORMS are primarily pests of cabbage-family plants but may at times feed on other garden vegetables, chewing holes in leaves. They hibernate as pupae and emerge as the familiar White Cabbage Butterflies. Several broods a year in warm climates.

CABBAGE LOOPERS, common throughout the U.S., feed on the underside of the leaves of cabbage and related plants. They crawl with a distinctive looping, or measuring-worm, movement. Cabbage Loopers winter as pupae attached to the underside of a leaf and emerge in spring as brown moths. Usually there are two or more generations a year.

DIAMONDBACK MOTH caterpillars eat small holes in the leaves of cabbage and related plants. Though seldom abundant, there may be local outbreaks. When disturbed, the worms wriggle rapidly and drop from the plant, hanging by a silken thread. Adult moths winter on the leaves of plants or in debris.

SQUASH VINE BORERS eat out the center of the stems of squash vines, causing them to wilt. They also attack pumpkins and, less commonly, cucumbers and muskmelons. Squash Vine Borers winter in the soil in silken cocoons. The moths, active during the day, lay their eggs at the base of plants, and the larvae burrow into the stems. Like other borers, these worms are hard to control because they work inside stems. Presence can be detected by the excrement (frass) pushed from hole in vine. Worms should be cut out by a lengthwise slit. After crop harvest, turn soil to expose the cocoons.

PICKLEWORMS bore into squash, muskmelons, and cucumbers, causing them to rot. Full grown after about two weeks of feeding, the worms roll the edge of a leaf over themselves and spin a thin layer of silk to form a pupa. Some cocoons remain attached to the plant; others drop to the ground. Adults emerge in about 10 days. Pickleworms reach a population peak late in the season; therefore, crops planted early are damaged least. Three or four generations are produced in a season. The related Melonworm feeds mostly on foliage. Both species are abundant pests in southern states, and the Pickleworm ranges as far north as Canada. To protect melons, squash are planted between the rows to collect the worms, which prefer the squash to the melons.

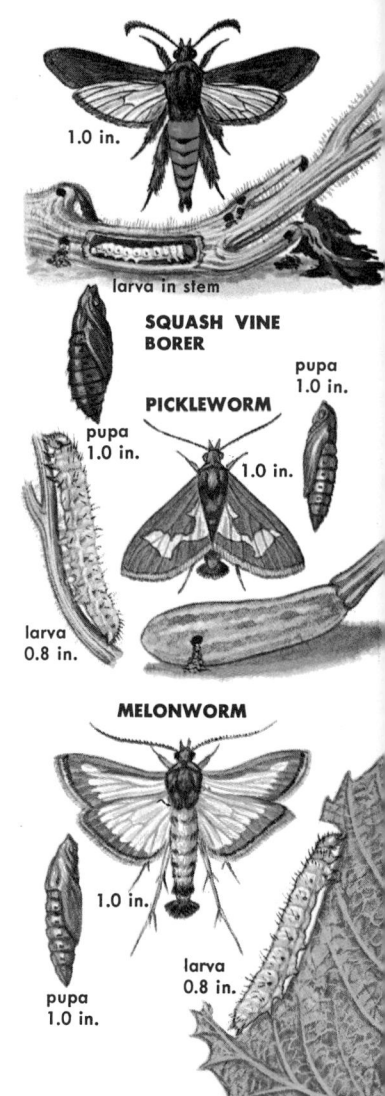

1.0 in.

larva in stem

SQUASH VINE BORER

pupa
1.0 in.

PICKLEWORM

pupa
1.0 in.

1.0 in.

larva
0.8 in.

MELONWORM

1.0 in.

larva
0.8 in.

pupa
1.0 in.

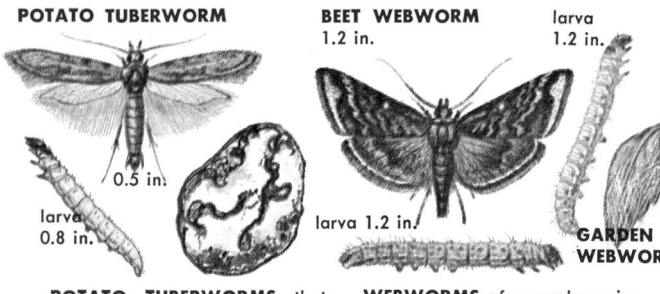

POTATO TUBERWORM

0.5 in.

larva
0.8 in.

BEET WEBWORM
1.2 in.

larva
1.2 in.

larva 1.2 in.

GARDEN WEBWORM

POTATO TUBERWORMS that hatch early in the season feed on leaves and stems of the potato plant. When full grown, in two to three weeks, each spins a silken cocoon in which it pupates on the ground. Adults emerge in about 10 days. Worms that hatch later in season tunnel into potatoes. Six generations may be produced in a year. Pull soil high around plants, as worms will not burrow deep. Cut, burn infested vines. Store potatoes where night-flying moths cannot lay eggs on them. Fumigate infested potatoes.

WEBWORMS of several species are general feeders on garden vegetables. In large infestations the worms migrate from one food plant to another. Webworms winter as larvae in silk-lined tubes and enter the pupa stage in the spring. Adults of the first generation emerge from March through June. The feeding worm spins a silken web that pulls together the edges of a leaf and anchors it to the ground. The worm hides in dirt at bottom of funnel. Can be killed with stomach-poison or contact insecticides.

TOMATO HORNWORM

pupa
2 in.

wingspread
to 5 in.

Five-spotted Hawkmoth
larva
3–4 in.

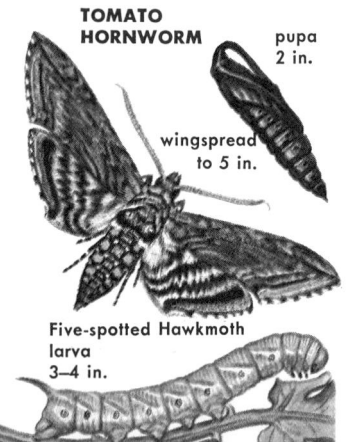

TOMATO HORNWORMS, also pests of tobacco, potatoes, and other related plants, pass the winter as hard-shelled pupae. The adults are large hawk moths that feed harmlessly on the nectar of deep-throated flowers such as petunias. Female moths lay their eggs on leaves of tomato plants, and the larvae feed ravenously, becoming full grown in about a month. They burrow into the soil to pupate. Two generations may be produced in a year in warm climates. The Corn Earworm (p. 109) and a number of cutworms (p. 64) burrow into tomatoes and feed inside.

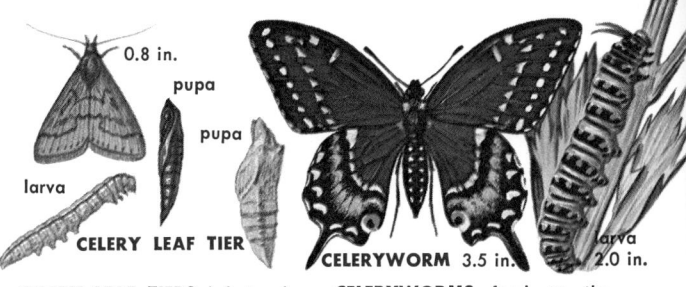

0.8 in.

pupa

pupa

larva

CELERY LEAF TIER

CELERYWORM 3.5 in.

larva 2.0 in.

CELERY LEAF TIERS infest celery, spinach, beets, and related plants, feeding on the leaves and tender growing parts and covering them with webs. When full grown, the worm pulls together the edges of a leaf and fastens them with silk. It pupates in a silken cocoon inside this roll. A complete life cycle takes about a month and a half, and in warm climates there may be several broods a year. Celery Leaf Tiers can be controlled with stomach-poison or contact insecticides, which should not be used on edible parts of plants.

WOOLLYBEARS are orange- or yellow-and-black caterpillars that feed on all kinds of garden vegetables. They may produce two broods per year. None of the several species are serious pests of particular plants. Some species hibernate as larvae, others in a cocoon made partly from their body hairs. They can be hand picked or killed with either contact or stomach-poison insecticides. The caterpillars roll into a ball when disturbed. In folklore the width of the bands on the caterpillar's body is said to forecast the winter—the more black, the colder the winter.

CELERYWORMS feed on the leaves of celery, parsnips, carrots, parsley, and related plants. When disturbed, the caterpillars protrude two orange horns near their head. The horns are soft and harmless, but at the same time the worm gives off a sweetish odor that apparently discourages predators. The butterflies (Black Swallowtails) overwinter in southern states. In the North the worms enter the pupa stage in winter. Celeryworms are seldom serious pests, and as they are large, they can be picked off the plants by hand.

Isabella Moth
1.5 in.

cocoon

BANDED WOOLLYBEAR

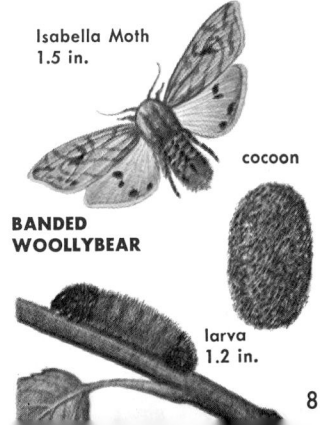

larva
1.2 in.

83

MAGGOTS (larvae) of some flies bore into stems or roots. Others, called leaf miners, feed on the tissues of leaves. The larvae pupate in the soil, and the adults lay their eggs on stems or leaves. Use contact insecticides to kill the adults, and stomach-poison insecticides for the maggots. Do not apply poisonous insecticides to plant parts that are to be eaten.

CABBAGE MAGGOTS are pests in northern U.S., where they feed on the roots of cabbage, turnips, radishes, broccoli, and similar vegetables. Infested plants wilt and may die. Several generations are produced in a year.

CARROT RUST FLIES lay their eggs at the base of plants, and the maggots work into the soil to feed on roots. Entire root systems of carrots, celery, parsnips, and related plants may be destroyed by these maggots.

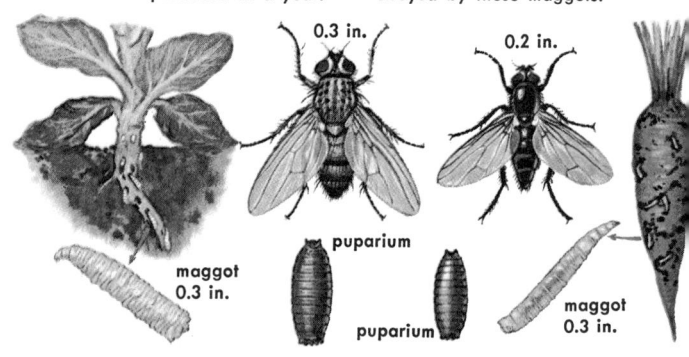

SPINACH LEAF MINERS infest beets, spinach, and other leafy vegetables, causing yellowish channels in leaves.

ONION MAGGOTS, especially bad pests in wet years, tunnel into onion bulbs. They are most abundant in northern states.

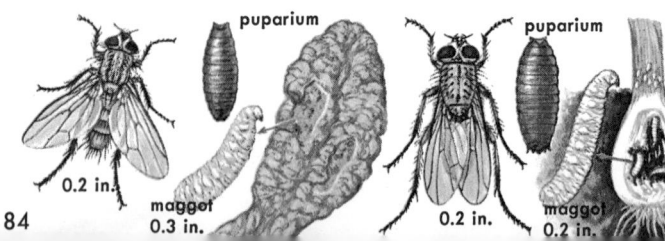

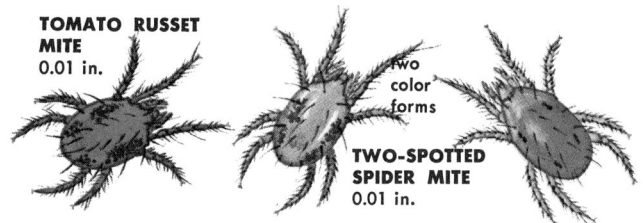

TOMATO RUSSET MITE 0.01 in.

two color forms

TWO-SPOTTED SPIDER MITE 0.01 in.

MITES, more closely related to spiders and ticks than to insects, are major pests of plants and also of man (p. 45) and his pets and domestic animals (pp. 54–55). Plant feeders suck the sap from leaves or tender parts of stems, causing them to become discolored. The injury weakens and may kill young plants. Many species spin, on the undersurface of leaves, a fine web containing their eggs and shed skins. Mites are most damaging in hot, dry weather, when a life cycle may be completed in as short a time as one week. Mites can be reduced in numbers by getting rid of weeds or other debris in which they pass the winter as adults or in the egg stage. Infested plants can be sprayed with a contact insecticide. Special miticides are also available. Consult a local agricultural agent.

SLUGS AND SNAILS are mollusks that sometimes feed on the foliage of vegetables. The damage may be mistaken for the feeding of insect pests. Slugs lack shells. Both slugs and snails leave a slimy trail. They usually feed at night and hide under debris during the day. Spread poison baits of calcium arsenate or metaldehyde mixed with bran, molasses, and water.

BROWN GARDEN SNAIL 0.8 in.

SPOTTED GARDEN SLUG 2–5 in.

Some insect pests of flowers and shrubs feed on a wide variety of plants, including vegetable and field crops. Others attack only one kind of plant. A greater range of chemicals can be used to kill insect pests on flowers and shrubs than can be risked on food plants, but follow carefully the directions for applying insecticides. Nearly all of these poisons are dangerous to people, pets, and domestic animals as well as to insects.

SCALES AND MEALYBUGS are among the most damaging of all insect pests of flowers and shrubs. Males of both mealybugs and scales can fly; females are wingless. Female mealybugs have legs and crawl slowly over stems and leaves as they feed. Soft scales, though legless, can move sluggishly but seldom do. Female armored scales, covered with a tough scale of wax mixed with shed skins of the nymph stages, fasten themselves permanently to a plant. A mealybug's body is covered with a cottony mass of wax that forms threadlike extensions. Scales and mealybugs suck the sap from leaves or stems, sometimes causing plants to wilt. If infestations go unchecked, a plant may die. Both mealybugs and scales produce large amounts of honeydew. The sweet excretion attracts ants, and patches of sooty mold grow where the honeydew drops beneath the infested plants. Mealybugs and scales can be killed with thiocyanate or nicotine-sulfate sprays, usually applied in white-oil emulsion. Parathion and malathion are also excellent controls but must be used with extraordinary caution. Rinse plants with a strong spray of water about an hour after application to prevent damage to the plant by chemical

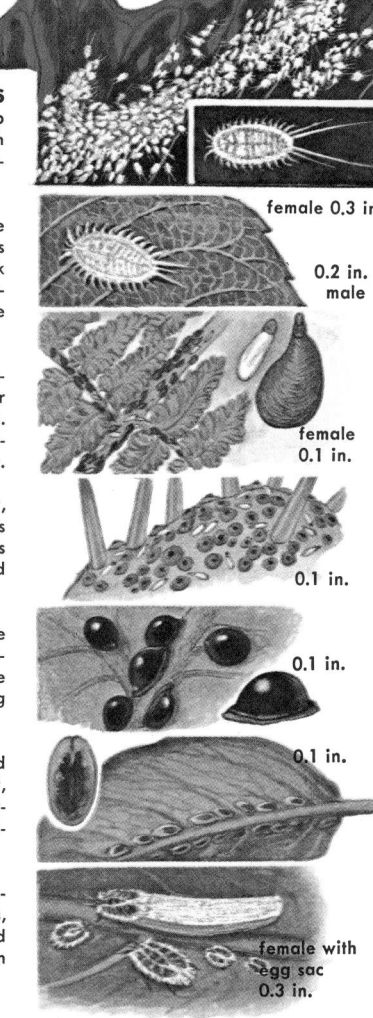

winged
male
0.3 in.

LONG-TAILED MEALYBUGS have long filaments at the tip of the body. Females give birth to nymphs. The Mexican Mealybug lays eggs.

MEXICAN MEALYBUGS are common pests in greenhouses and in warm climates attack plants outdoors. Hollyhocks, geraniums, and chrysanthemums are frequent victims.

FERN SCALES are pests of bananas, orchids, citrus, and other plants outdoors in warm climates. In cool climates they occur indoors on ferns and other plants.

CACTUS SCALES are abundant, armored scales, found outdoors in southwestern U.S. or indoors on plants in greenhouses and homes.

HEMISPHERICAL SCALES are pests in warm climates or on indoor plants. Oval scales become strongly convex. Flat young scales are notched at rear.

BROWN SOFT SCALES, flat and close to the color of their host, are pests in greenhouses; outdoors on gardenias and oleanders in warm climates.

GREENHOUSE ORTHEZIAS, related to scales and mealybugs, are pests in greenhouses and outdoors, attacking more than 100 species of plants.

female 0.3 in.

0.2 in. male

female 0.1 in.

0.1 in.

0.1 in.

0.1 in.

female with egg sac 0.3 in.

FLOWERS AND SHRUBS 87

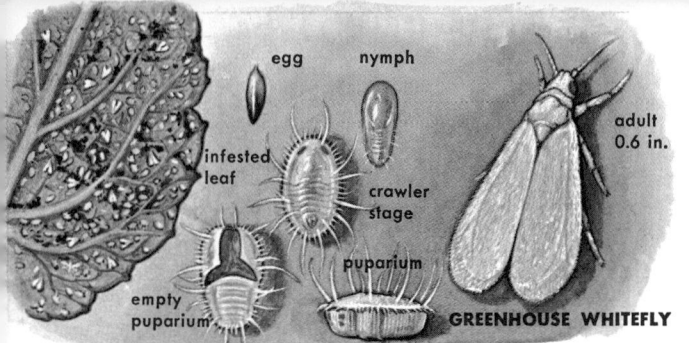

egg   nymph

infested leaf

crawler stage

adult 0.6 in.

puparium

empty puparium

GREENHOUSE WHITEFLY

WHITEFLIES in large numbers may feed unnoticed on the underside of leaves until the white-winged adults are disturbed and take flight. Both the adults and nymphs suck sap from stems and leaves, causing an infested plant to wilt. In warm climates whiteflies are pests outdoors the year around; in cool climates they are principally pests in greenhouses or on plants kept in the home. Some species, such as the common Greenhouse Whitefly, spread outdoors during the warm months. Like aphids, whiteflies excrete honeydew. These pests can be killed with oil sprays and also with the organo-phosphate insecticides.

APHIDS are pests of flowers and shrubs. All aphids have similar life histories and habits. A few species feed on the roots of plants, but most kinds suck sap from leaves or stems. Control of aphids on ornamentals is the same as for vegetables (p. 66).

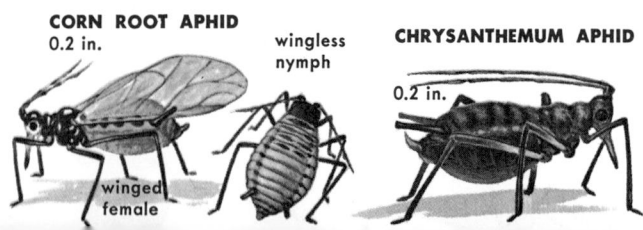

CORN ROOT APHID
0.2 in.

wingless nymph

CHRYSANTHEMUM APHID

0.2 in.

winged female

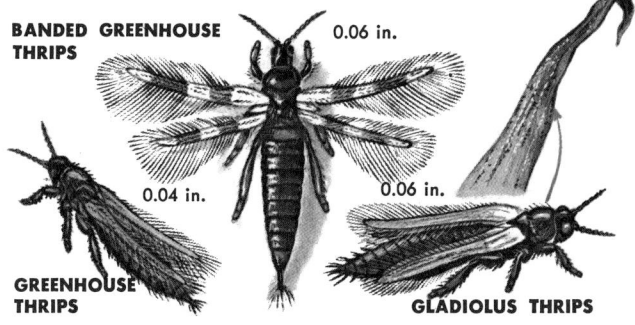

BANDED GREENHOUSE THRIPS 0.06 in.

0.04 in.

0.06 in.

GREENHOUSE THRIPS

GLADIOLUS THRIPS

THRIPS, pests of a variety of plants, are much alike in appearance and life history (p. 72). Most thrips attack shrubs and flowers, particularly in warm climates, and they are especially damaging in greenhouses. The Greenhouse Thrips is found throughout the world. The Banded Greenhouse Thrips is a prevalent pest in western U.S., while the Gladiolus Thrips is distributed throughout the U.S. on gladioli, irises, and lilies. The leaves of infested plants turn white or silvery and then brown due to the loss of sap drawn out by the feeding thrips. Thrips can be killed with contact insecticides, and bulbs can be dusted with insecticide when stored.

TREEHOPPERS, related to leafhoppers (p. 68), lay eggs in crescent-shaped slits cut in twigs. Fungi develop in the slits, and the scarred twigs do not grow well. Nymphs of treehoppers suck the juices from grasses, lilies, and other plants. Spray with contact insecticide.

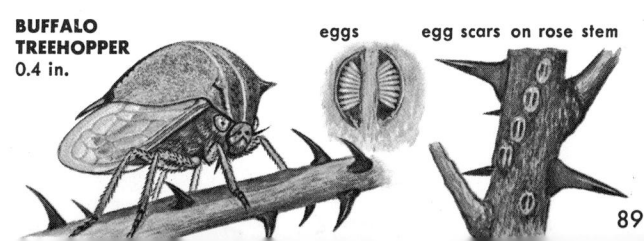

BUFFALO TREEHOPPER 0.4 in.

eggs

egg scars on rose stem

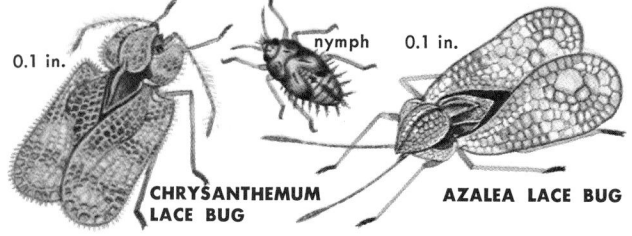

0.1 in.

nymph

0.1 in.

CHRYSANTHEMUM LACE BUG

AZALEA LACE BUG

LACE BUGS, both the handsome adults and the spiny nymphs, suck juices from leaves or stems. They damage ornamentals and also vegetable plants (p. 73). Leaves of infested plants are spotted with dark, shiny excrement. Lace bugs overwinter as eggs attached to leaves and in warm weather produce two or more broods in a season. Contact insecticides should be used to kill adults or nymphs as soon as they appear.

MITES damage plants in greenhouses and attack a great many kinds of plants outdoors in warm weather. They are pests also of vegetables (p. 85), man (p. 45), and domestic animals (p. 54—55).

CYCLAMEN MITES attack cyclamens, delphiniums, marigolds, other garden flowers, and also strawberries. They feed on tender leaves in the plant's crown and also overwinter there. Foliage turns black. Immerse suspected seedlings in water at 110 degrees F. for about 20 minutes before setting them out.

BULB MITES attack roots, corms, and bulbs of such plants as lilies, crocuses, hyacinths, gladioli, and tulips. Infested bulbs turn soft, and the stem of the plant breaks over. Destroy infested bulbs by burning or burying them deeply. Or immerse bulbs in water at 110 to 115 degrees F. for an hour and a half.

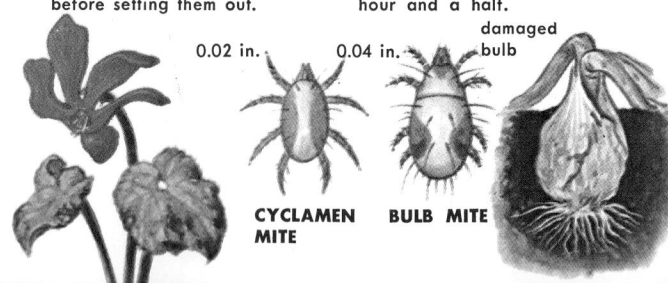

0.02 in.

0.04 in.

damaged bulb

CYCLAMEN MITE

BULB MITE

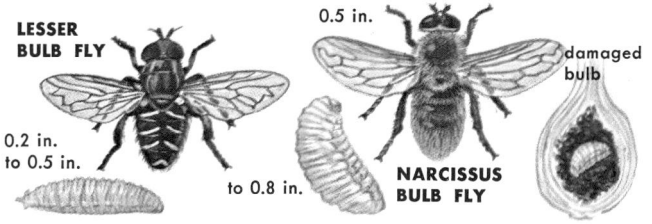

LESSER BULB FLY

0.5 in.

damaged bulb

0.2 in. to 0.5 in.

to 0.8 in.

NARCISSUS BULB FLY

BULB FLIES attack bulbs of lilies, narcissuses, irises, hyacinths, and such root crops as onions, carrots, and potatoes. The maggots feed inside the bulbs, opening them to fungi. They pupate in the bulb or in the soil. The Lesser Bulb Fly produces two broods a year, the Narcissus Bulb Fly one. Maggots of the Lesser Bulb Fly usually infest already weakened or injured bulbs, and many maggots may occur in one bulb. Only one maggot of the Narcissus Bulb Fly is ordinarily found in a bulb. In early spring, when the adult flies lay their eggs, cover plants with cheesecloth. At harvest, destroy bulbs that feel soft and are probably infested. Treat the others in hot water, as for Bulb Mites (p. 90).

MIDGES are small flies. Some species, such as larvae of the Chrysanthemum Gall Midge, form galls on stems or leaves. Maggots of the Rose Midge feed on buds and new shoots, deforming and causing them to die. Full-grown maggots burrow into the soil to pupate. Remove and destroy infested parts of plants. Treat soil with a contact insecticide; spray plant to kill larvae.

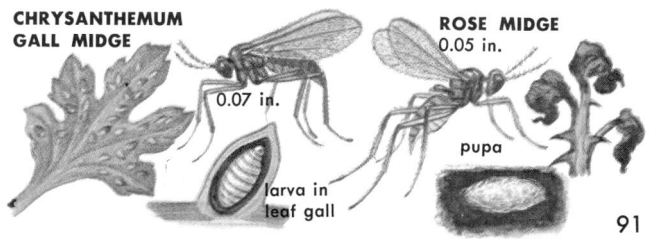

CHRYSANTHEMUM GALL MIDGE

0.07 in.

larva in leaf gall

ROSE MIDGE

0.05 in.

pupa

91

LEAF MINERS, the larvae of certain moths, flies, beetles, or sawflies, feed between the epidermal layers of a leaf, causing blisters, blotches, or tunnels. In time the leaves turn brown and drop off.

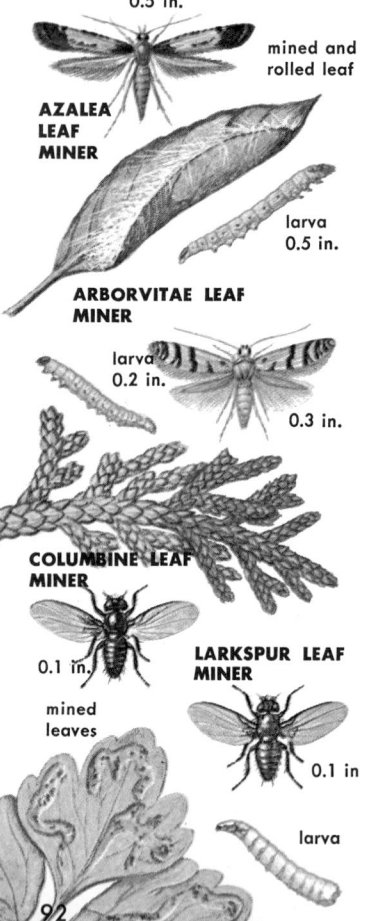

0.5 in.

mined and rolled leaf

AZALEA LEAF MINER

larva 0.5 in.

ARBORVITAE LEAF MINER

larva 0.2 in.

0.3 in.

COLUMBINE LEAF MINER

0.1 in.

LARKSPUR LEAF MINER

mined leaves

0.1 in

larva

AZALEA LEAF MINERS, the caterpillars of a small moth, feed in the leaf tissues until about half grown, then emerge and feed at the tip or margin. The caterpillar rolls or folds the leaf over itself and feeds inside this cover, in which it also pupates. Leaf rolls can be pulled off and destroyed. Dust plants with a stomach-poison insecticide to kill larvae feeding on surface.

ARBORVITAE LEAF MINERS eat out the inside of needles at the branch tips. The caterpillars overwinter in the branches and emerge in late spring or early summer. Females lay eggs on the foliage. Cut and destroy infested tips. Adults and newly hatched larvae should be killed with a contact insecticide.

COLUMBINE LEAF MINERS, also pests on asters, are fly larvae. As many as a dozen larvae attack one leaf. Infested leaves should be burned or buried. Spray plants with a contact insecticide.

LARKSPUR LEAF MINERS mine in leaf tissues of delphiniums. Adult flies puncture the under-surface of leaves, turning them brown. Destroy infested leaves. Spray or dust plants with a contact insecticide. Cultivate soil to kill pupae.

BORERS feed inside stems, leaves, fruit, or roots. They are difficult to reach with sprays or dusts. An infected plant wilts and in time dies or breaks off. Bacteria and fungi enter the plants through the holes made by borers.

COLUMBINE BORERS lay eggs on the ground or in debris near plants. A fall cleanup of debris destroys many eggs. Contact insecticides in soil at base of plants kill caterpillars.

LILAC BORER caterpillars winter inside the stem. Cut off and burn infested stems. Or kill borers inside holes in stems with a wire probe or squirt in a few drops of carbon bisulfide.

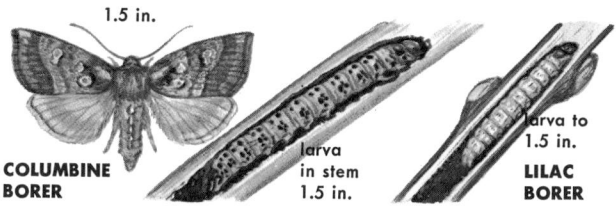

1.5 in.

COLUMBINE BORER

larva in stem 1.5 in.

larva to 1.5 in.

LILAC BORER

LEAF ROLLERS twist or roll a portion of a leaf over themselves and fasten it together with silk. They feed on the surface or at the edge of the leaf, and when full grown, pupate inside the roll. The two most common species of leaf rollers, attacking a wide variety of flowers and shrubs, are the Oblique-banded and the Red-banded. Both stomach-poison and contact insecticides are effective controls and should be applied as soon as damage is discovered.

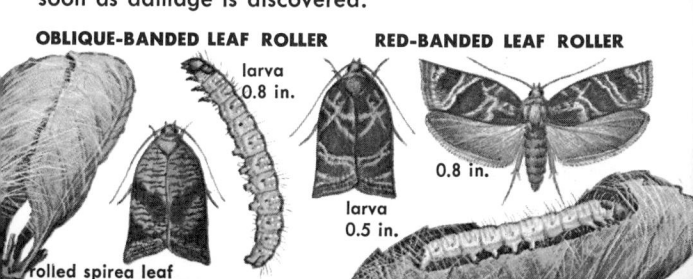

OBLIQUE-BANDED LEAF ROLLER

larva 0.8 in.

RED-BANDED LEAF ROLLER

0.8 in.

larva 0.5 in.

rolled spirea leaf

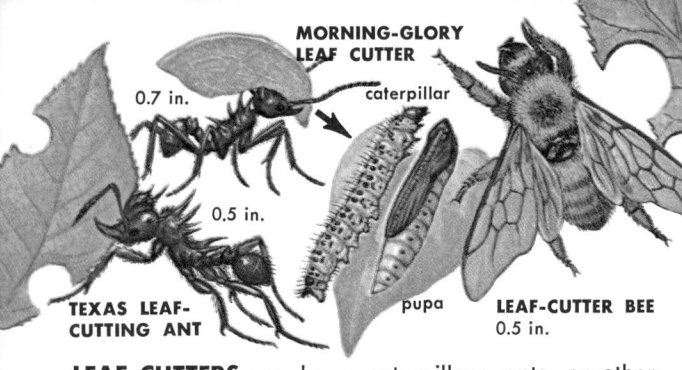

MORNING-GLORY LEAF CUTTER

0.7 in.

caterpillar

0.5 in.

TEXAS LEAF-CUTTING ANT

pupa

LEAF-CUTTER BEE
0.5 in.

LEAF CUTTERS are bees, caterpillars, ants, or other insects that cut large pieces from leaves. Leaf-cutter ants, found in Louisiana, Texas, and southward, take the pieces of leaves to their nest and chew them up to make a mulch on which fungus grows. Leaf-cutting bees roll the piece of leaf into a thimble shape to line the stem cavity in which the larva is feeding. The Morning Glory Leaf Cutter cuts off the leaves of morning glories, zinnias, dahlias, and other flowers. The caterpillars feed at night and hide during the day in the wilted leaves. Use stomach poisons as dusts or sprays.

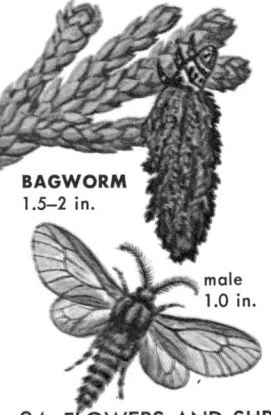

BAGWORM
1.5–2 in.

male
1.0 in.

BAGWORMS move about in a bag of tough silk, covered with needles or twigs. Especially damaging to conifers. In late summer the caterpillars form pupae inside the bags. Winged males emerge in the fall and mate with the wingless females, which lay their eggs inside the bag and never emerge. Bags can be picked by hand, or plants sprayed with a stomach-poison insecticide while larvae are feeding.

SAWFLIES belong to the same order of insects as bees and wasps. Instead of stingers, the females have a saw-tooth-edged ovipositor with which they cut slits in leaves or bore holes into stems to lay eggs. The larvae of sawflies resemble caterpillars of moths and butterflies and, like them, feed on foliage.

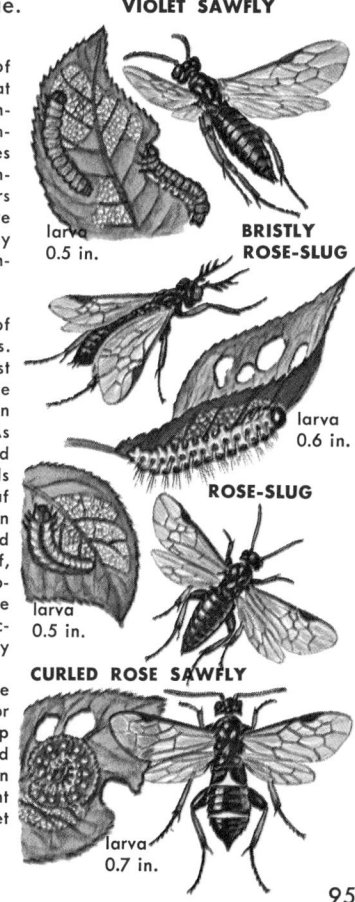

VIOLET SAWFLY

VIOLET SAWFLIES, pests of both violets and pansies, feed at night. They first eat out the underside of the leaf and skeletonize it. Then they eat holes through the leaf and may completely defoliate a plant. Blisters are formed on the leaves where the females lay eggs. Spray plants with a stomach-poison insecticide.

larva
0.5 in.

BRISTLY ROSE-SLUG

ROSE-SLUGS are the larvae of several species of sawflies. Bristly Rose-slug larvae feed first on the undersurface of the leaves, skeletonizing them, then eat holes through the leaves. As many as six broods are produced in a season. The Rose-Slug feeds on the upper surface of the leaf and produces one generation in a season. Larvae of the Curled Rose Sawfly eat the whole leaf, usually feeding in a curled position like a grub. Slugs can be killed with stomach-poison insecticides applied to leaves in early stages of the feeding.

larva
0.6 in.

ROSE-SLUG

larva
0.5 in.

The Bristly Rose-slug and the Rose-Slug pupate in debris or loose soil; hence a fall cleanup destroys the pupae. The Curled Rose Sawfly larvae pupate in woody or pithy stems. Paint pruned ends of stems and get rid of debris.

CURLED ROSE SAWFLY

larva
0.7 in.

BLACK BLISTER BEETLES are pests of asters, zinnias, chrysanthemums, anemones, and other flowers. They commonly eat the petals in preference to the leaves. The Black Blister Beetle resembles the Striped Blister Beetle (p. 74) in life history and habits and is controlled by the same methods.

0.8 in.

BLACK BLISTER BEETLE

BEETLES Some of the many species of beetles feed on the foliage, flowers, stems, roots, or fruit of shrubs and flowers. Some are damaging only in the larva, or grub, stage; others do their greatest damage as adults. Both larvae and adults have chewing mouthparts. Some are pests in both stages. Many beetles are general feeders; others attack only one kind or related plants.

ROSE LEAF BEETLES feed on the blossoms of irises and peonies as well as roses. They also eat leaves, blossoms, buds, and young fruit of pears, plums, apples, peaches, strawberries, and others. They can be hand-picked or jarred into a pail of kerosene and water. They feed deep in flowers or buds and are hard to reach with insecticides. Pyrethrum or other contact insecticides are effective.

ROSE CHAFERS are general pests of flowers and shrubs and also of many fruit and vegetable crops. Adult beetles appear in late spring or early summer, feeding first on the flowers and then on foliage. The larvae feed on the roots of grass and burrow deep into the soil to hibernate. Adults can be hand-picked, or infested plants can be sprayed. Rose Chafers are deadly poisonous to chickens.

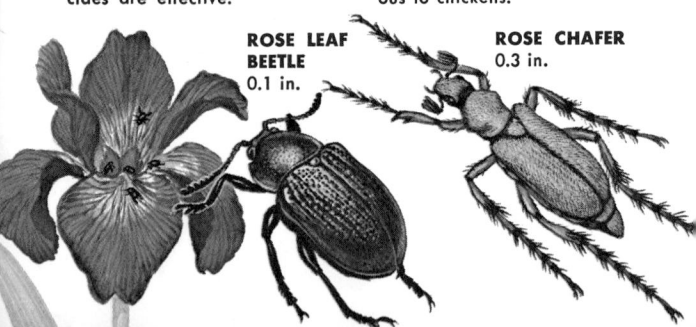

ROSE LEAF BEETLE
0.1 in.

ROSE CHAFER
0.3 in.

FULLER ROSE BEETLES are weevil pests (p. 78) of roses, carnations, geraniums, gardenias, chrysanthemums, azaleas, and many other shrubs and flowers. Adults feed at night, eating the margins of the leaves. The grubs feed on the roots, causing the foliage to turn yellow. They can be controlled by the same methods used for the Rose Curculio.

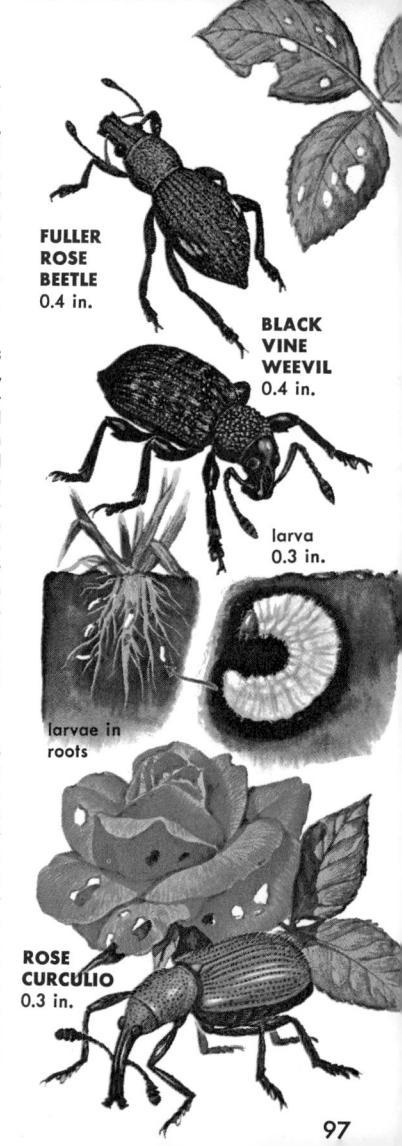

FULLER ROSE BEETLE
0.4 in.

BLACK VINE WEEVIL
0.4 in.

larva
0.3 in.

larvae in roots

ROSE CURCULIO
0.3 in.

BLACK VINE WEEVILS are pests of gardenias, azaleas, begonias, spirea, arborvitae, rhododendron, and many other flowers and shrubs. The larvae feed first on the root hairs of plants and then on larger roots, stripping them of bark. The grubs hibernate in winter, feed again on the roots in spring, then form pupae and emerge as adults in early summer. The adult weevils (p. 78) are active at night, eating foliage for about a month before laying eggs in soil. Spray or dust with a stomach-poison or a contact insecticide.

ROSE CURCULIOS are weevils (p. 78) with especially long snouts, or beaks. They eat holes in the stems or unopened buds of roses. Injured buds may not open, or if they do, the petals are filled with holes. The larvae develop in the young fruit or hips, and when full grown, drop to the ground to pupate. Beetles can be hand-picked or jarred from the plant into a container of water and kerosene. Dust plants with a stomach-poison or contact insecticide. Destroy infested rose hips.

FIELD AND FORAGE CROP PESTS

All field crops are food for insects. Losses average 10 percent, but in epidemic outbreaks entire crops are lost.

GRASSHOPPERS About 600 species of grasshoppers inhabit North America. Ninety percent of the damage is due to five species that attack field crops; more than 20 species are damaging to grasslands. The dry grasslands east of the Rocky Mountains, where the annual rainfall is less than 30 inches, periodically have grasshopper outbreaks in which the crop losses amount to millions of dollars. Most species of grasshoppers are general feeders, though they prefer young, green plants. In epidemic outbreaks the hungry hordes will eat any food available. They will strip a tree or bush of its foliage and then feed on the bark. In heavy outbreaks, with 50 or more grasshoppers to the square yard, grass is cropped close and permanently injured, exposing the land to wind and water erosion.

Most grasshoppers lay eggs in late summer or early fall. The female pushes her ovipositor as deep as two inches into the soil, depositing her eggs in packets consisting of as many as 100 eggs. These masses of eggs, glued together with particles of soil, are called pods. Each female may lay as many as a dozen pods. The eggs hatch in the spring, and the nymphs begin eating immediately. The number of times they shed before becoming adults varies with the species but is usually five or six. Most species produce only one generation a year, but the Migratory Grasshopper and several others may produce two generations in warm climates. Plowing or disking the land in the fall buries some of the eggs so that the nymphs cannot make their way to the surface.

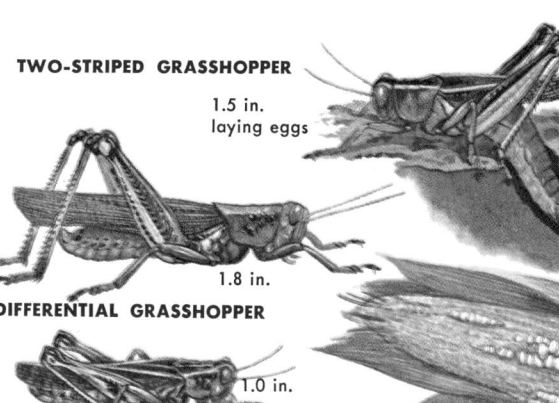

TWO-STRIPED GRASSHOPPER

1.5 in.
laying eggs

1.8 in.

DIFFERENTIAL GRASSHOPPER

1.0 in.

CLEAR-WINGED GRASSHOPPER

These five species of grasshoppers are the most damaging to field and forage crops in the United States. The ear of corn above has only a few scattered kernels because grasshoppers ate off silks before pollination.

MIGRATORY GRASSHOPPER

RED-LEGGED GRASSHOPPER

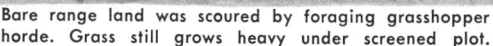

Bare range land was scoured by foraging grasshopper horde. Grass still grows heavy under screened plot.

Others are exposed to the weather or to predators. Poisoned baits (sweetened bran containing arsenic, chlordane, or similar poisons) are used effectively to kill adults, and large areas in western states are sprayed with contact insecticides from airplanes.

APHIDS damage plants by sucking the sap from the stems, leaves, or roots. They stunt the plant's growth, or in heavy infestations cause it to die. Aphids have complex life cycles (p. 66).

GREENBUGS are aphid pests of grains. In warm climates they are active throughout the year. In cool climates males and females are produced in late summer. They mate, and the females deposit eggs in the folds of leaves. Greenbugs are parasitized by a small wasp that lays its eggs in the aphid's body. The wasp's larvae feed on the aphid's internal organs. In a cool spring, the aphids build up a large population before the wasps become active. Plow under volunteer crops. Plant resistant varieties. Use contact insecticides to check infestations of Greenbugs.

CORN ROOT APHIDS infest the roots of corn. The corn grows well until about a foot tall and then becomes stunted and yellowed. The aphids winter in the egg stage, stored in the nests of the Cornfield Ant. As soon as they hatch in spring, the young are pastured first on the roots of weeds or grasses, then on corn plants. The aphids produce winged generations that fly to other plants, where they are captured by ants and put to work. The ants eat the honeydew expelled by the aphids. Ant nests should be destroyed by plowing or by treating the soil with a contact insecticide.

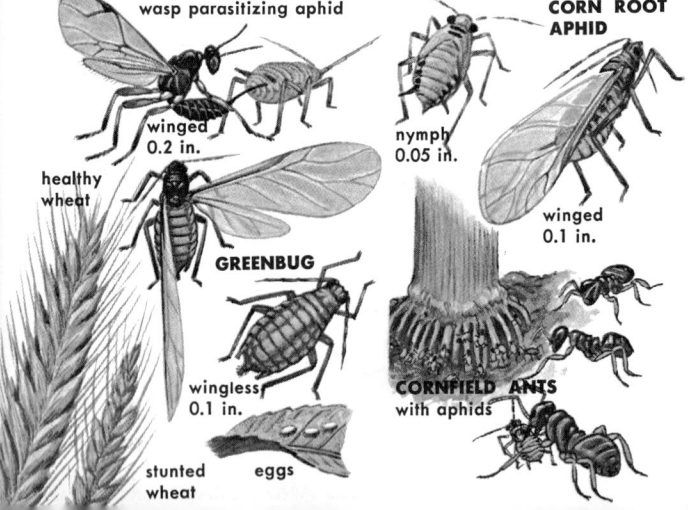

wasp parasitizing aphid

winged
0.2 in.

healthy
wheat

GREENBUG

wingless
0.1 in.

stunted
wheat

eggs

**CORN ROOT
APHID**

nymph
0.05 in.

winged
0.1 in.

CORNFIELD ANTS
with aphids

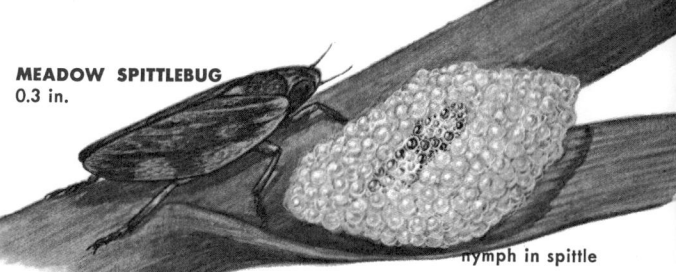

MEADOW SPITTLEBUG
0.3 in.

nymph in spittle

SPITTLEBUGS damage plants as nymphs, sucking the juices from stems or leaves. The nymphs surround themselves with a mass of froth, or spittle, as they feed. The squat, broad adults are sometimes called froghoppers. The Meadow Spittlebug, a pest of alfalfa and other legumes and also of many ornamentals, produces only one generation in a season. The nymphs hatch from eggs laid in stubble. Spray plants with contact insecticides before fall harvest to kill egg-laying adults or in early spring to kill young nymphs.

PLANT BUGS, also called leaf bugs, are a family of true bugs containing many species that damage and deform plants by sucking out juices. Some feed on only one group of plants, such as grasses; others, such as the Tarnished Plant Bug (p. 71), are general feeders.

LEGUME BUGS are pests of legumes and other plants. Nymphs are most damaging, but adults also feed on plants. Both introduce a toxin causing deformities. Adults overwinter, and females lay their eggs in plant tissues in spring, with four or five generations produced in a season. Use a contact insecticide in spring when nymphs begin to feed. Do not spray plants in flower, thus killing bees that pollinate crop.

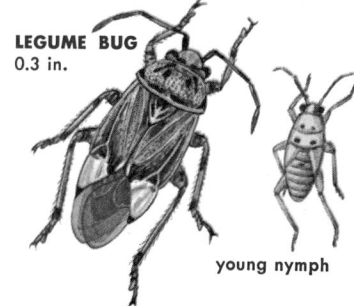

LEGUME BUG
0.3 in.

young nymph

red nymph 0.2 in.

CHINCH BUG

CHINCH BUGS are major pests of corn but also damage other grains and grasses. Adults overwinter in debris, and in the spring the females lay eggs at the base of plants, on which the nymphs feed by sucking out juices. Young plants are commonly killed; older plants survive but may not produce. As food plants are exhausted in one place, the nymphs migrate in droves to find new food plants. Chinch Bugs can be killed with contact insecticides sprayed or dusted on infested plants, or the insecticides may be used as a chemical barrier to prevent entry of crawling nymphs. Some crop varieties are resistant to Chinch Bugs. Crop rotation prevents population buildup.

CEREAL LEAF BEETLES, from Europe, were first found in the U.S. in 1962 and are now a potential major pest of grain crops in the Midwest. Adults survive cold winters by hibernating under debris. The larvae hatch from eggs laid in early spring and feed on the leaves of young plants. They pupate in June, and adults appear in July, feeding until winter.

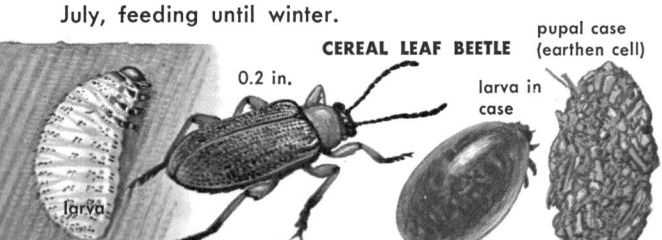

CEREAL LEAF BEETLE

pupal case
(earthen cell)

0.2 in.

larva in case

larva

ROOTWORMS are grubs, or beetle larvae, that injure plants by feeding on or in their roots. Often the adults damage entirely different plants.

NORTHERN CORN ROOTWORMS, which feed only on corn, are pests from New York westward to the Rocky Mountains, especially in the northern Mississippi Valley. Infested plants grow slowly and are weakened so that they topple in wind or heavy rain. The larvae also transmit wilt, a bacterial disease. In midsummer the larvae leave the roots and pupate in the soil. The adults, which feed on a variety of plants, die after laying eggs around roots of cornstalks in the fall. Eggs hatch the following spring. Rotating crops is effective. Chemical controls include soil treatment with contact insecticide before plowing, or sprays or dusts on adults.

SOUTHERN CORN ROOTWORM damage is similar to injury by the Northern Corn Rootworm, but worms also bore into stalks at soil line. Adults are equally damaging.

GRAPE COLASPIS grubs (Clover Rootworms) feed on the stems and foliage of grapes and other plants. Adult beetles emerge in midsummer and lay their eggs around roots of cover crops such as clover. The grubs feed on the roots until cold weather, then hibernate until spring, when they continue feeding. If a field is plowed in spring and then planted in corn, the half-grown grubs feed on roots. Fall plowing exposes grubs to freezing.

SOUTHERN CORN ROOTWORM

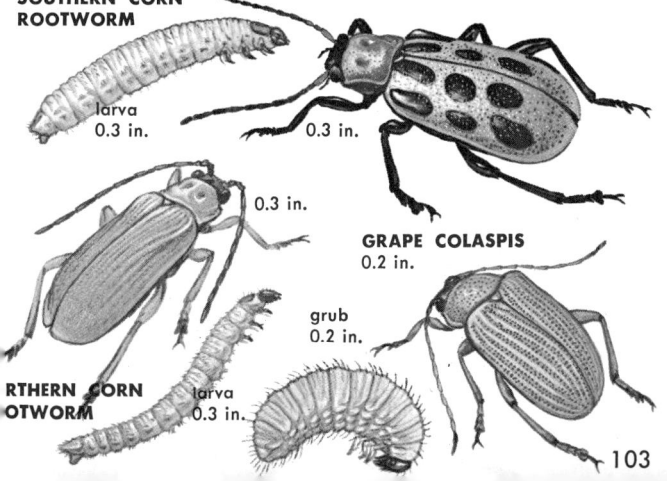

larva
0.3 in.

0.3 in.

0.3 in.

GRAPE COLASPIS
0.2 in.

grub
0.2 in.

RTHERN CORN
OTWORM

larva
0.3 in.

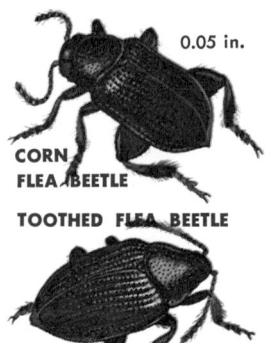

CORN FLEA BEETLE
0.05 in.

TOOTHED FLEA BEETLE
0.05 in.

ORIENTAL BEETLE
0.7 in.

grub
1.0 in

WHEAT WIREWORM
0.3 in.

0.8 in.
1.0 in.

1.0 in.

PLAINS FALSE WIREWORM

FLEA BEETLES, especially abundant in cool, wet seasons, attack many field and garden crops. In addition to eating leaves and generally weakening a plant, they transmit the bacteria for Stewart's disease, a wilt. Heavy infestations sometimes cause a complete loss of crops. Keep fields free of weeds under which the beetles hibernate in winter. For other controls see p. 62.

WHITE GRUBS of a number of species eat the roots of lawn grasses, corn, wheat, and forage crops. Infested corn plants may die after growing to a height of about two feet. In addition to the grubs of May and June beetles, larvae of the Oriental Beetle are serious pests. Control by soil fumigation and by other methods described on p. 65.

WIREWORMS of several species injure corn, wheat, lawn grasses, and root crops. The Plains False Wireworm, particularly damaging to wheat, is a darkling beetle larva rather than a click beetle as are true wireworms. Controls are given on p. 63.

WEEVILS, the largest family of beetles, are easily recognized by their long snout, at the end of which are their chewing mouthparts. When disturbed, many weevils "play dead." Some weevils are pests of vegetable crops (p. 78), fruits (p. 125), and stored products (p. 146). Many are as damaging in the grub, or larva, stage as they are as adults.

ALFALFA WEEVILS, important pests in western U.S., winter as adults in debris on the ground. In spring they emerge and feed on alfalfa or other legumes. The females lay their eggs in cavities chewed into the stems. At first the grubs feed where they hatch; later they move up to the tips. Often the plant is stunted, and the entire first-growth crop may be lost. When full grown, the larvae spin cocoons, and the adults appear in about ten days. Adults can be killed with contact insecticide. Consult agricultural agent for best time to apply and for advice on use of sprayed crop as livestock feed.

BILLBUG is a name used for several species of snout beetles that attack corn, wheat, and other grains. Adult Maize Billbugs eat holes in the stems and leaves of corn. The grubs, even more damaging, feed on the taproots and in the pith of the stalks, forming pupae in late summer or early fall. Adults hibernate in winter. Crop rotation is an effective control for the Maize Billbug and the similar, more southern Curlewbug. Maize Billbugs can be destroyed in hibernation by raking a field and burying debris. The Bluegrass Billbug feeds on wheat, timothy, and other grasses in the grub stage.

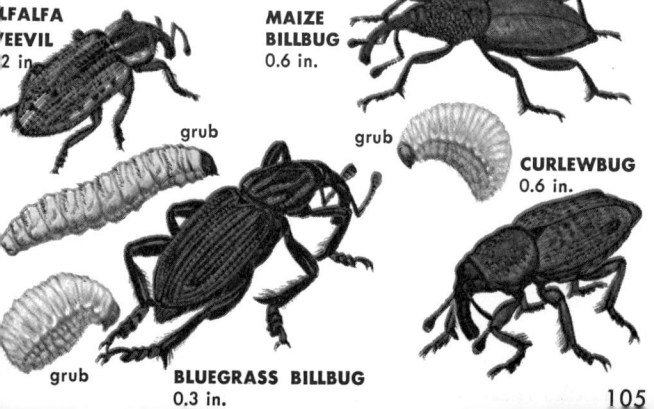

LFALFA
EEVIL
2 in

grub

MAIZE
BILLBUG
0.6 in.

grub

CURLEWBUG
0.6 in.

grub

BLUEGRASS BILLBUG
0.3 in.

CLOVER LEAF WEEVIL
0.3 in.

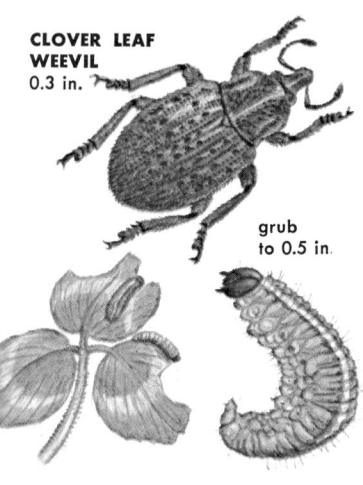

grub
to 0.5 in.

CLOVER LEAF WEEVILS, also pests of alfalfa, are most damaging in early spring and may destroy an entire crop. The grubs feed on leaves at night and hide beneath plant during the day. They complete growth by late spring and spin a cocoon in the soil or on the plant. Adults emerge in early summer. After a brief period of feeding they become relatively inactive until fall, then mate and the females lay eggs. Larvae that hatch in the fall hibernate until spring. Some eggs do not hatch until spring. In wet seasons many larvae are killed by fungus disease. A field can be plowed and planted in grass, or crop sprayed with a contact insecticide.

SWEETCLOVER WEEVIL
0.2 in.

CLOVER ROOT CURCULIO
0.2 in.

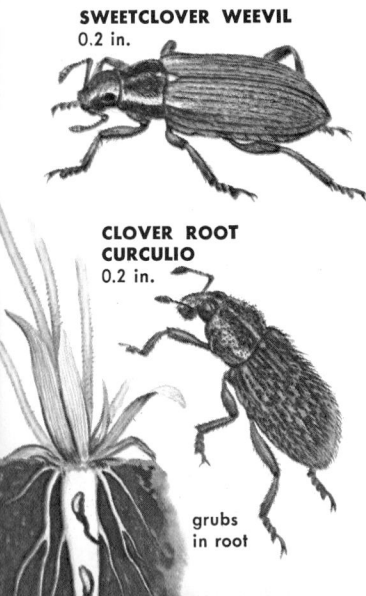

grubs
in root

SWEETCLOVER WEEVILS and closely related Clover Root Curculios are pests of nearly all legumes. The grubs burrow into the roots, causing plants to wilt and die. These weevils usually overwinter as young larvae, though in some regions they pass the winter in the egg or adult stage. Larvae complete their development by late spring, then form pupae and emerge as adults by summer. Adults feed on foliage for about a month, after which they become less active until fall, when they begin to feed again. At this time they mate and females lay eggs on food plant. Control is difficult. Fields can be plowed in early spring or late fall and planted in grass or other non-legume plant. Contact insecticides will kill weevils but may make crop unusable as a livestock food.

LESSER CLOVER LEAF WEEVILS are most damaging to red clover but may also attack alfalfa and sweetclovers. The damage, greatest in dry seasons, is done largely by the grubs, which feed on the stems, leaves, and buds. An infested plant wilts and dies. No good control methods have been discovered.

BOLL WEEVILS are one of the more than 100 insect pests of cotton. As many as seven generations of Boll Weevils are produced in a season, damaging the plant at all stages of its growth. Each generation completes its development in about three weeks in good weather. Adults that emerge from hibernation in debris near cotton fields begin feeding on the buds of young cotton plants. The females lay one egg in a deep puncture in each developing flower bud, or square. If not enough squares are available, more than one egg may be laid in a square. The larvae feed in the square, causing it to turn yellow and drop. In heavy infestations the bloom of an entire crop is destroyed. When bolls do form, the weevils feed inside. Young bolls drop from the plant; older ones are stained or decay. Controls consist of destroying cotton stalks or debris in which adults hibernate, planting early maturing varieties of cotton, and using contact insecticides to kill the feeding larvae and adults. Timing is critical in the success of these controls and varies with local conditions. Consult regional agricultural agent.

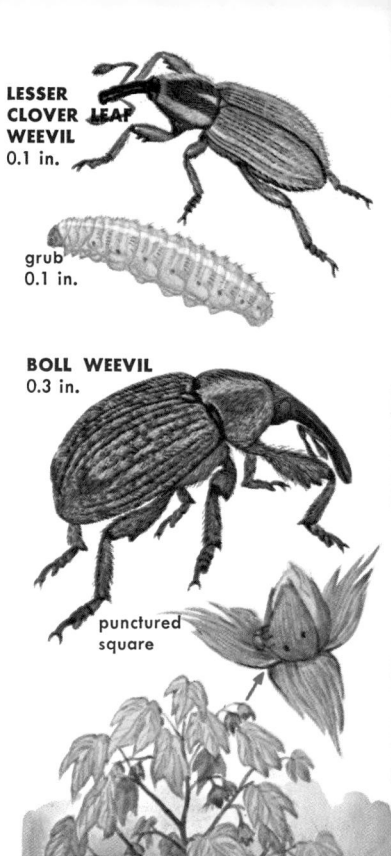

LESSER CLOVER LEAF WEEVIL
0.1 in.

grub
0.1 in.

BOLL WEEVIL
0.3 in.

punctured square

grub from boll
0.3 in.

CATERPILLARS of moths and butterflies are common pests of field and forage crops. Methods of combating them are much the same as those used in controlling caterpillars that damage vegetable crops (p. 80). All have strong chewing mouthparts.

COTTON LEAFWORMS crawl by looping their body, like measuring worms. Unlike almost all other moths, the adults may be pests, using their spiny mouthparts to make slits in grapes, peaches, or other fruit to get the sweet juices. The larvae hatch from eggs laid on the underside of cotton leaves. Later they pupate in folded leaves. A life cycle is completed in about a month, with as many as three or four generations a season. No stage survives winter in the U.S., the pest invading each year from Central America. Both stomach-poison and contact insecticides are effective controls.

PINK BOLLWORMS feed on cotton blossoms, or squares, causing them to wilt and drop. Later they feed in the bolls. Pink Bollworms winter in cocoons in the soil, inside bolls, or in the seed. Larvae may remain in this resting stage for more than two years, which accounts for the world-wide spread of this pest. Each generation requires about a month, with as many as six generations a season. Worms in the seed are killed by heat (145 degrees F.) or by fumigation. Early crops give harvests before the pests are numerous. Plow under crop residues or use contact insecticides. Consult local agricultural agent for timing.

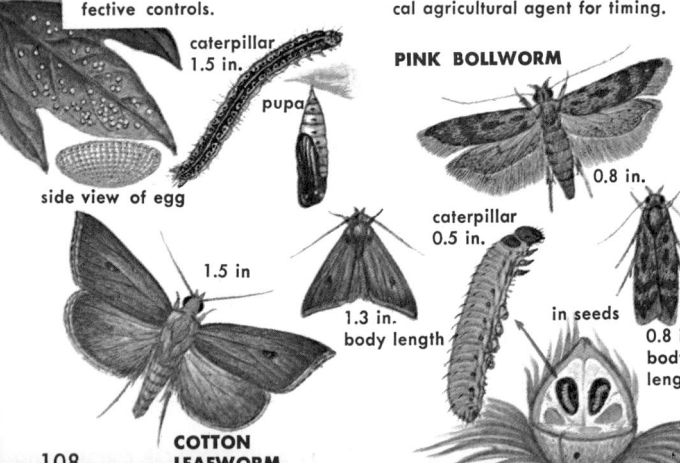

caterpillar
1.5 in.

pupa

side view of egg

PINK BOLLWORM

0.8 in.

caterpillar
0.5 in.

1.5 in

1.3 in.
body length

in seeds

0.8 i
body
leng

COTTON LEAFWORM

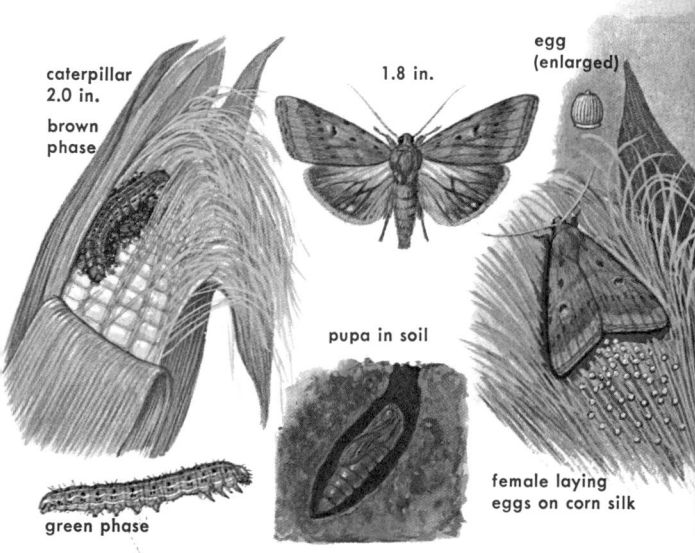

caterpillar
2.0 in.

brown phase

1.8 in.

egg (enlarged)

pupa in soil

green phase

female laying eggs on corn silk

CORN EARWORMS, known as Bollworms and Tomato Fruitworms, are the major pests of sweet corn in the U.S. From 500 to more than 2,000 eggs are laid by each female. The larvae feed on the unfolding leaves, sometimes stunting the plants. Greatest damage occurs when the corn is in the tassel, or silk, stage, as the larvae that hatch on the silks feed there and also on the developing kernels. In addition to destroying the kernels, the larvae open avenues for molds and for other insect pests. The worms feed also on the flowers of tomatoes and eat the green fruit. They feed on the buds of tobacco plants and in the seed pods. In cotton-growing areas they feed on the tips of the plants, on the blossom, and in the bolls. Up to seven generations are produced each year in warm climates; three or four in the Corn Belt, only one in northern states. Corn Earworms overwinter in the soil in a pupa case, hence plowing in late fall destroys many or exposes them to freezing temperatures. Feeding worms can be killed with contact-insecticide dusts. Some hybrid corn varieties are resistant to Corn Earworms. Early maturing varieties can be harvested before the pest population builds up.

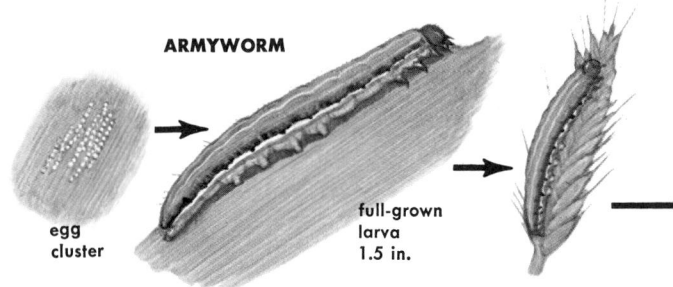

ARMYWORM

egg
cluster

full-grown
larva
1.5 in.

ARMYWORMS hibernate as half-grown caterpillars that begin feeding in spring and are full grown by early summer. They burrow into the soil, pupate, and emerge as night-flying moths that are identified by the white dot on each front wing.

Female moths, after a period of feeding on nectar or decaying fruit, lay their eggs on grass or other plants. Larvae hatch in about a week and begin feeding ravenously on the plants around them. If conditions have been favorable, many thousands of caterpillars are produced. When the plants are consumed in one area, the hungry hordes move in "armies" to find a new sup-ply. Caterpillars of this second, or summer, generation become full grown in late summer. They pupate, and the adults emerge in the fall, each female laying as many as 2,000 eggs, in clusters of 25 to 100. These hatch into the larvae that overwinter.

The summer generation does the greatest damage, and in the years of severe outbreaks many crops are attacked and completely destroyed. The caterpillars hide during the day and feed at night; hence a crop may be destroyed completely before the caterpillars are noticed. Armyworms are parasitized by a fly that lays its eggs on the caterpillar's back; the fly's larvae

FALL ARMYWORM

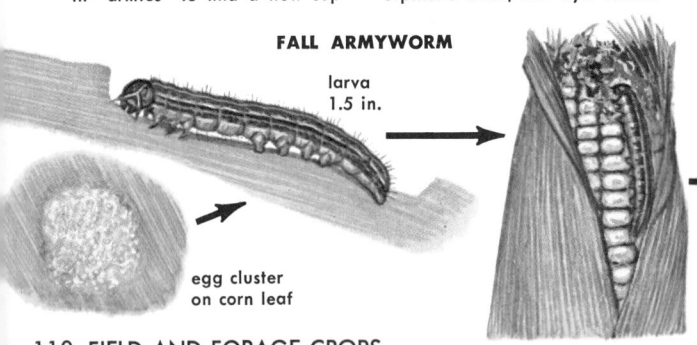

larva
1.5 in.

egg cluster
on corn leaf

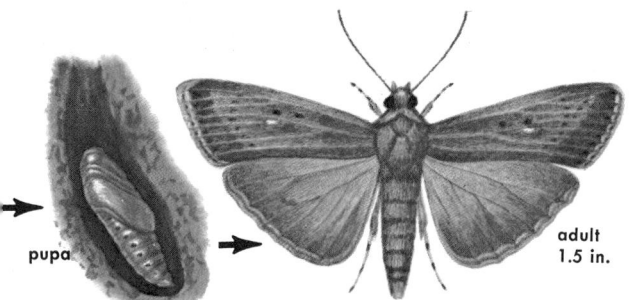

pupa

adult
1.5 in.

then feed on the caterpillar and kill it. A tiny wasp that lays its eggs inside the Armyworm's eggs is an even more effective natural control of this pest.

Advancing "armies" of these caterpillars can be trapped in deep furrows containing kerosene or a contact insecticide. Poison-bran baits such as those used for grasshoppers (p. 98) can be spread in the path of the migrating caterpillars, or fields can be sprayed with contact insecticides. When the worms disappear, indicating that they have burrowed into the ground to pupate, shallow plowing will expose the pupae to predators and to weather.

FALL ARMYWORMS are a southern species closely related to the Armyworms. Sometimes the moths fly into northern states, appearing there in the fall. They do not survive northern winters, however. In the South as many as six generations are produced in one season. The caterpillars feed first on grass, then move to corn or other field and vegetable crops. In the South the caterpillars go by the name of Grass Worms. Fall Armyworms do not hide during the day as do Armyworms. In addition to the controls effective against the Armyworm, it is important to keep fields free of grass on which the larvae feed first.

pupa

adult
1.3 in.

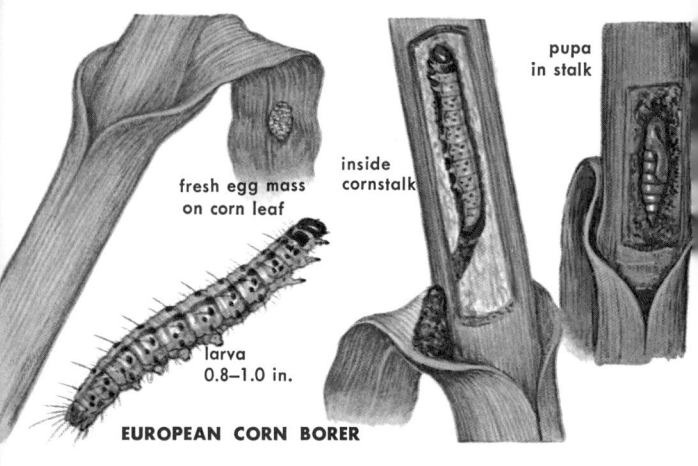

fresh egg mass
on corn leaf

inside
cornstalk

pupa
in stalk

larva
0.8–1.0 in.

EUROPEAN CORN BORER

EUROPEAN CORN BORERS are the most injurious pests of corn in the U.S. From their point of introduction in the Boston area, just before 1917, they have spread across the continent to the Rocky Mountains.

Originally the European Corn Borer produced only one generation each season, but in the East it now usually produces two. Though corn is preferred, the caterpillars, particularly those of the second generation, will feed on many other kinds of plants. European Corn Borers overwinter as caterpillars in the stems of food plants. In the spring they pupate in the stem, emerging as night-flying adult moths in about 10 days. During the day the moths stay in hiding under the corn leaves or in weeds nearby. The female moth lays her eggs in flat clusters of a dozen or more on the underside of the leaves of food plants. Each female may lay a total of nearly 2,000 eggs, which are at first white but later turn yellowish.

Newly hatched larvae are yellowish. They feed first on the leaves, then bore into the stem or the ear, where they feed until full grown, in about a month. Where there are two generations per year, the first is completed by midsummer, and the larvae of the second generation are full grown by winter.

Often many borers attack a single plant, weakening it and causing it to fall over. Food canals in the cornstalk are cut off so that ears of corn do not form properly. Borings are also openings for other insect pests and for rot fungi.

Stems and stalks in which borers might hibernate should be plowed under in the fall or early spring. Resistant varieties of

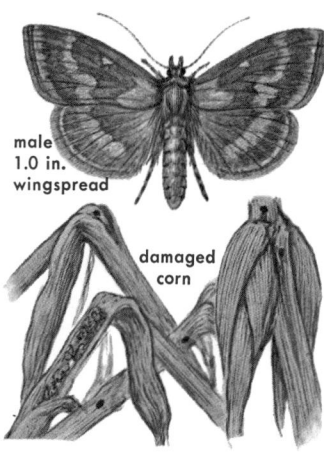

male
1.0 in.
wingspread

damaged
corn

TOBACCO HORNWORMS are the large caterpillars of attractive moths. They overwinter as a distinctive chrysalis, with its tongue in a separate handlelike projection. The handle is longer than the closely related Tomato Hornworm's (p. 82). The giant caterpillars are ravenous feeders on the leaves of many plants. They can be destroyed by hand-picking them, or if especially abundant, with insecticides. Fall plowing to expose the pupae is also effective. At rest, caterpillars hold front of body erect in a stiff sphinxlike pose. The naked pupa has a distinctive handle in which the proboscis fits. Swift-flying adults are called sphinx or hawkmoths.

corn should be planted. Some hybrid varieties give a good yield of corn even though infested with borers. Late planting of any variety will reduce the infestations but may also lower the yield of corn. Where economical to do so, corn may be rotated with legumes. Of the many natural enemies that biologists have introduced from Europe, the most effective are three species of wasps and a species of fly, all of which parasitize the caterpillars. Contact insecticides can be applied to infested plants either as dusts or sprays, but their effectiveness depends to a great degree on proper timing. Generally the insecticide is applied when 70–80 percent of the plants in a field show signs of infestation. Local agricultural agents can advise the time and recommended rates of spray per acre for use in a particular area.

CAROLINA SPHINX

4–5 in.
wingspread

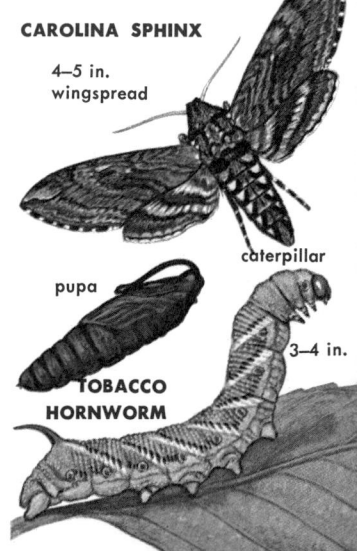

caterpillar

pupa

3–4 in.

TOBACCO HORNWORM

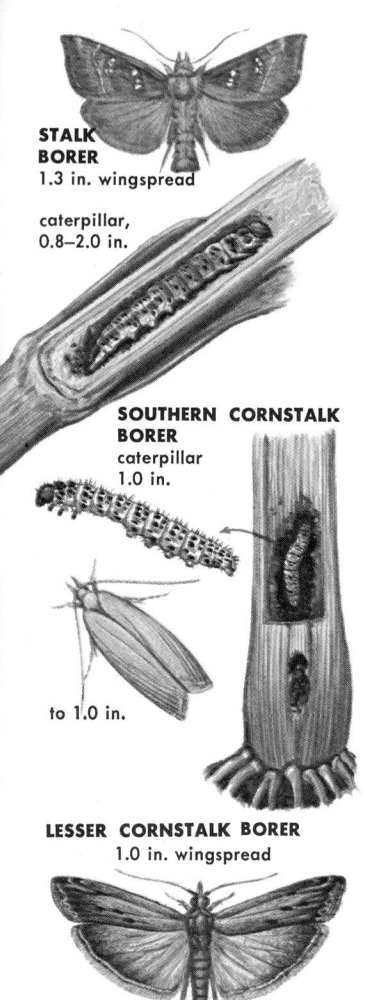

STALK BORER
1.3 in. wingspread

caterpillar,
0.8–2.0 in.

SOUTHERN CORNSTALK BORER
caterpillar
1.0 in.

to 1.0 in.

LESSER CORNSTALK BORER
1.0 in. wingspread

caterpillar
0.8 in.

STALK BORERS are moths that overwinter as eggs attached to grass or weeds. The eggs hatch in early spring, and the larvae bore immediately into the stem of a plant, usually the one on which the eggs were laid. Later the caterpillars move to giant ragweeds, corn, and other large plants. In August they pupate, either in the stem or in the soil nearby, and emerge as adult moths in late summer or early autumn. The females lay eggs before winter. Stalks and debris should be plowed under in fall.

SOUTHERN CORNSTALK BORERS are pests from southern U.S. to South America. The similar Southwestern Cornstalk Borer occurs only in southwestern United States and Mexico. Infested corn is stunted, the stalks enlarged or swollen. Ears are poorly formed and may drop. The caterpillars overwinter in the cornstalks, change to pupae in early spring, and emerge as adults before summer. As many as three generations are produced in a season. Destroy stalks harboring hibernating larvae; rotate corn with legumes.

LESSER CORNSTALK BORERS, pests in southern U.S., bore into the base of cornstalks and also legumes, stunting and deforming the plants. They usually overwinter as larvae, forming pupae in late winter and emerging as adults in early spring. Two generations are produced in a season. Destroy stalks in which larvae overwinter.

WEBWORMS are general feeders, though some species are especially damaging to lawns or to particular field crops. Bluegrass Webworms and related species are lawn pests. They feed only at night, cutting off blades of grass and dragging them into their silk-lined tunnels formed along the surface of the ground. The adult moths, which have a prominent snout, are commonly seen flying over grassy areas at dusk. The Corn Root Webworm (illustrated) attacks corn, tobacco, and other crops as well as grasses in which they hibernate. Plowing is an effective control for pests of field crops. Lawns can be treated with a contact insecticide.

ALFALFA CATERPILLARS feed on alfalfa and other legumes. Winter is passed in the pupa stage, from which butterflies emerge in early spring. Females lay eggs on the leaves of plants, on which the larvae feed. There may be seven generations a year. Plants can be sprayed with a contact insecticide if the crop is not used for hay.

CLOVER HEAD CATERPILLARS feed in the clover head, preventing flowers from opening, or on green developing seeds. First-generation moths appear in early summer and lay eggs on clover plants, where the larvae feed and pupate. Three generations may be produced each season. Early cutting of crop destroys many larvae. The larvae are also parasitized by a wasp.

CORN ROOT WEBWORM
1.0 in. wingspread

larva
0.5 in.

at rest

webbing and damage
to corn roots

ALFALFA CATERPILLAR
1.5 in. wingspread

larva
1 in.

CLOVER HEAD CATERPILLAR
0.3 in.

larva
0.3 in.

FLY MAGGOTS of only a few species are serious pests of field and forage crops. They damage plants in the same ways as do larval pests of vegetable crops (p. 84). feeding inside the stem, flowers, or seeds.

CLOVER SEED MIDGES winter as larvae in a thin cocoon in the soil or under debris. They enter the pupa stage in the spring and emerge as adult flies in late spring. Within a few days the females deposit eggs in young clover heads, using their long ovipositor to reach deep inside. The developing larvae feed by sucking the sap from the flower parts, thus preventing the formation of seed. When full grown, in about a month, the larvae drop to the ground to pupate. Adults of this generation appear in midsummer and lay eggs that hatch into the overwintering larval forms. The best means of control is cutting the clover before it is in full bloom.

WHEAT STEM MAGGOTS are minor pests of wheat. In the fall they feed in the lower stem of the plant. Their damage is similar to that done by the Hessian Fly (p. 117). In summer the maggots feed near the wheat heads. Infected stems eventually turn white and die. Oats, barley, rye, and other grasses are also attacked. Wheat Stem Maggots overwinter as larvae inside the stem of their food plant. They form pupae in the spring and emerge as adult flies in early summer. A second generation starts in summer, and these larvae overwinter. Crop rotation and destruction of straw in which the larvae are feeding are effective controls.

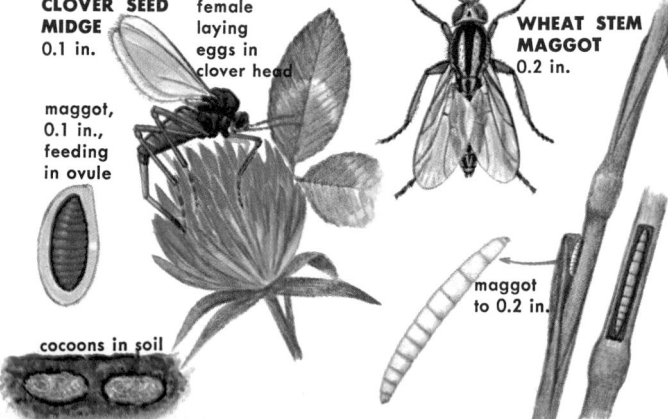

CLOVER SEED MIDGE
0.1 in.

female laying eggs in clover head

maggot, 0.1 in., feeding in ovule

cocoons in soil

WHEAT STEM MAGGOT
0.2 in.

maggot to 0.2 in.

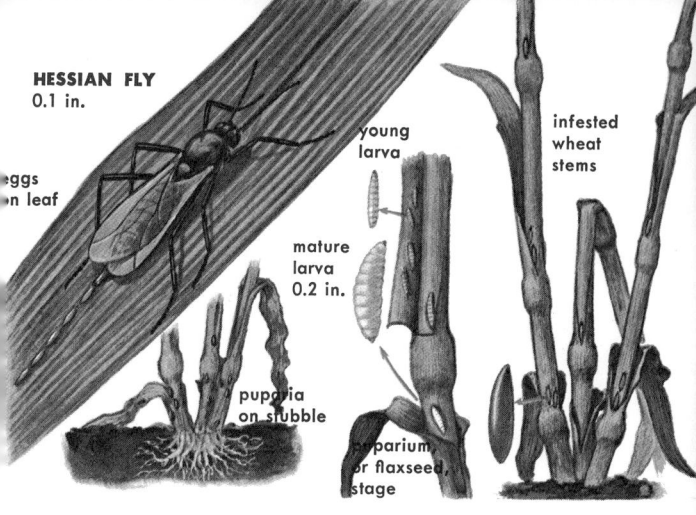

HESSIAN FLY
0.1 in.

eggs on leaf

young larva

infested wheat stems

mature larva 0.2 in.

puparia on stubble

puparium or flaxseed stage

HESSIAN FLIES are the most damaging pests of wheat. They also attack barley, rye, and some species of wild grasses. The feeding of the larvae stunts the plant's growth or kills it if the infestation is heavy. Plants that survive give poor yields. Secondary fungus infections also occur. The life history of the Hessian Fly varies with the region and the wheat-growing method.

In winter-wheat plantings, eggs are laid on leaves of wheat that come up in late summer or fall, and the maggots move down the leaf to where it joins the stem and begin sucking out the plant's juices. Growth is completed in two to six weeks. The larvae then form pupae in their last larval skin. The flat puparia look like flaxseeds. Adult flies emerge in the spring, and within a few days the females begin laying eggs on the leaves of the wheat plants. Again the larvae feed at the point of juncture of the leaf with the stem and form pupae before the wheat is ready for harvest. Adult flies emerge in late summer and lay eggs that start a second generation on the winter wheat.

Where spring wheat is grown, the second generation is completed earlier, and the flies overwinter also as pupae. If fall planting can be delayed, the flies are unable to lay their eggs on the leaves in time for the larvae to complete development before cold weather. A local agricultural agent can specify the proper time for planting. Volunteer wheat should be destroyed, as should the stubble after a harvest. Resistant varieties of wheat have been developed, and crops should be rotated where possible. Systemic insecticides are now available.

SAWFLIES AND CHALCIDS are among the few insect pests of plants that belong to the large order containing bees, wasps, and ants.

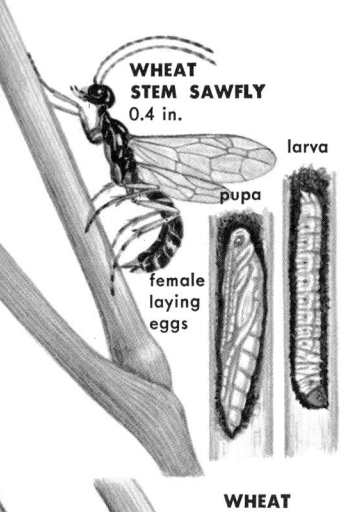

WHEAT STEM SAWFLY
0.4 in.

female laying eggs

larva

pupa

WHEAT STEM SAWFLIES are destructive to wheat and other small grains. The larvae feed inside the stems, working from the top of the plant, where the eggs are laid, toward the bottom. Near the ground level the larvae eat out the inside of the stem completely, causing it to break off. The larvae plug the open base with droppings and then pass the winter in this chamber. Pupae are formed in the spring, and adult sawflies emerge in early summer. The best control is plowing under stubble. Planting corn, legumes, or other crops not attacked by the Wheat Stem Sawfly prevents buildup of pests. Resistant varieties of wheat are available.

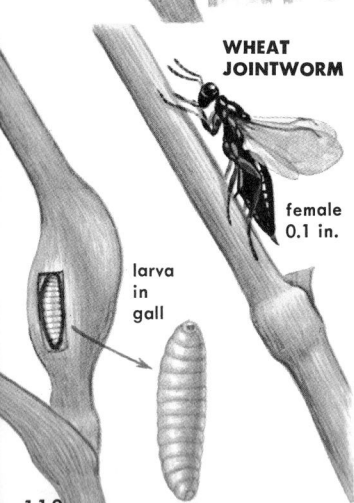

WHEAT JOINTWORM

female
0.1 in.

larva in gall

WHEAT JOINTWORM damage is similar to the injury done by the Hessian Fly, causing the wheat plants to break over. The break occurs at a gall-like swelling on the inside of which are the feeding maggots. Adult females have a stiff ovipositor, with which they drill a hole into the stem of a wheat plant just above a joint. Inside the stem they lay from one to two dozen eggs. The feeding of the larvae on the tissues causes the stem to swell and twist. The full-grown larvae remain in the stem, wintering either as larvae or as pupae. Adults emerge in spring. Wheat stubble should be plowed under or burned.

WHEAT STRAW-WORMS have two generations a year. Young plants are attacked in the spring and stunted by larvae that eat into the stem and developing heads. Larvae of the first generation, full grown by May, form pupae in the plant stem and emerge as winged adults by early June. The females deposit their eggs in wheat stems, usually only one egg per stem, and the larvae feed inside through the summer. They pupate in the fall and emerge from the straw or stubble as wingless adults in early spring. They look much like ants. The females lay eggs on young wheat, thus renewing the cycle. Crop rotation is effective. Stubble and volunteer wheat should be plowed under.

CLOVER SEED CHALCIDS destroy the seeds of alfalfa and clovers. The larvae winter inside the seeds on the ground, forming pupae in early spring and emerging as adults in late spring. The tiny adults lay their eggs in the formed but still soft seeds, which then become food for the larvae. Adults are produced from this generation by midsummer, and another generation is started. In warm climates there are as many as three generations. There is no good control for this pest.

THIEF ANTS are not only household pests (p. 24) but may also be field pests. They prefer protein foods, but will eat corn and other seeds. Best control is cultivation of field to break up ant nests.

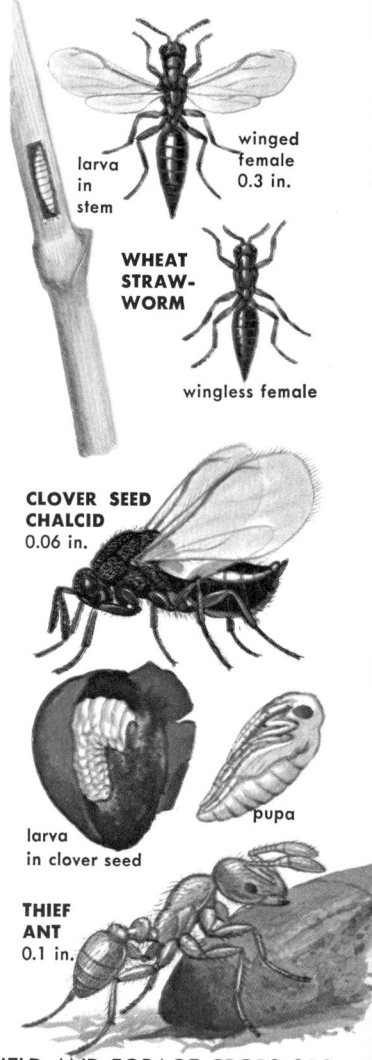

larva in stem

winged female 0.3 in.

WHEAT STRAW-WORM

wingless female

CLOVER SEED CHALCID 0.06 in.

larva in clover seed

pupa

THIEF ANT 0.1 in.

FIELD AND FORAGE CROPS 119

PESTS OF FRUITS AND FRUIT TREES

Entire fruit crops are sometimes lost because of insect pests. Some species attack through the roots, trunk, branches, or leaves. Other insects attack only the fruit. Some do damage in only one stage of their life history, while others are pests both as larvae and as adults.

CATERPILLARS of moths and butterflies form the largest group of insect pests attacking fruit and fruit trees. A few caterpillars feed only on the fruit. Many others are leaf feeders.

CODLING MOTHS are the most damaging pests of apples. They also attack pears, quinces, and other fruits. Adults appear in the spring and are active at dusk, the females laying their eggs on leaves, twigs, or fruit spurs. The worms at first feed on the leaves but soon crawl to the developing fruit and burrow inside, feeding near the core and on the seeds. When their growth is completed, usually in about a month, the larvae crawl to the outside and either drop to the ground or crawl down the trunk. They spin a cocoon under debris or loose bark and pass the winter in full-grown larval stage, transforming in spring into pupae and emerging as adults in about two weeks. In most areas there are two generations a year. The first is completed in midsummer; larvae of second generation overwinter.

Control consists of cleaning up debris, including the loose bark on trees, to eliminate places where larvae spin cocoons. Trees can be sprayed with contact insecticides to kill larvae before they enter fruit. Do not spray until petals have fallen from flowers, as early spraying will kill honeybees visiting the blossoms. Do not spray within two weeks of harvest.

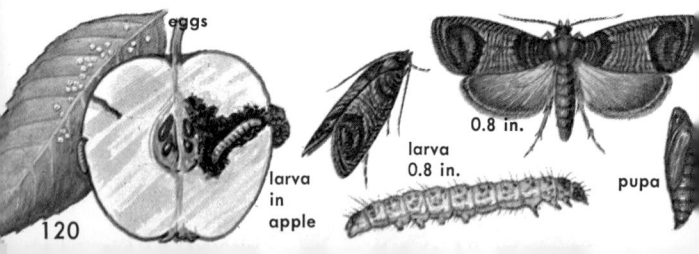

eggs

larva in apple

larva 0.8 in.

0.8 in.

pupa

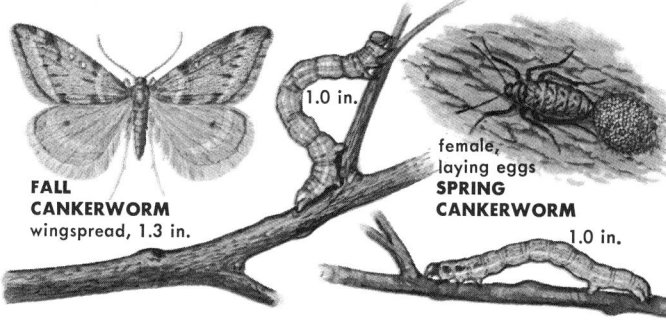

FALL CANKERWORM
wingspread, 1.3 in.

1.0 in.

female, laying eggs
SPRING CANKERWORM

1.0 in.

CANKERWORMS eat leaves of trees and shrubs, often defoliating them. The caterpillars move with a looping motion. Inchworms and Measuring Worms are other names for these caterpillars. Spring Cankerworms have three pairs of true legs on the thorax and two pairs of prolegs on the abdomen. In crawling, the rear of the body is brought forward so that the hind legs are against the front legs, the center of the abdomen forming a loop. Then the front part of the body is stretched forward full length. If disturbed, worm drops on a silk thread.

Adult moths of the Spring Cankerworm emerge from the pupae in early spring. Males are winged, females wingless. The females lay their eggs in clusters on the bark of trees. As soon as they hatch, the larvae move to the leaves, which are usually just coming out, and begin feeding. After about a month the full-grown caterpillars drop

to the ground and pupate, emerging the following spring.

Fall Cankerworms have a similar life history, but the adult moths emerge from the pupae in the fall and lay eggs that do not hatch until spring. The caterpillars have three pairs of prolegs at the end of the abdomen rather than two as in the Spring Cankerworm.

Both pests can be controlled by painting a band of contact insecticide around trunk of tree to kill wingless females that crawl up the trunks to lay eggs. Spray foliage to kill larvae.

BUD MOTHS of several species feed on the young buds of pear, apple, and other fruit trees. The caterpillars overwinter in silken cases attached to twigs and begin feeding in early spring. They form pupae and emerge as adults by midsummer, starting a second generation. They can be controlled by spraying with contact insecticides.

EYE-SPOTTED BUD MOTH

larva
0.5 in.

wingspread, 0.6 in.

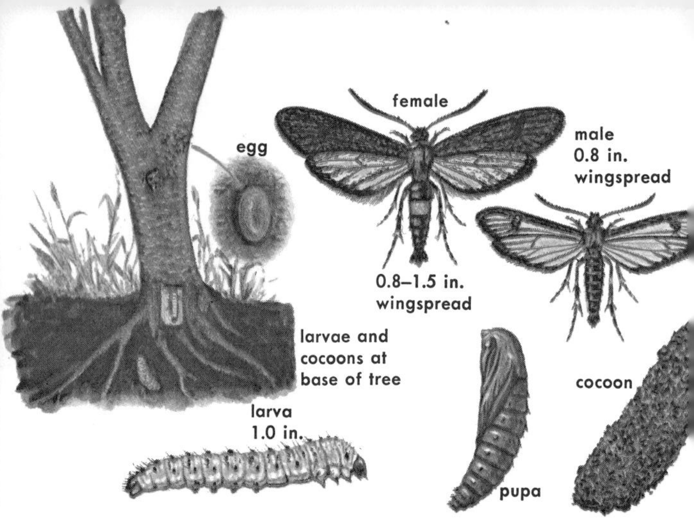

female

male
0.8 in.
wingspread

egg

0.8–1.5 in.
wingspread

larvae and
cocoons at
base of tree

cocoon

larva
1.0 in.

pupa

PEACH TREE BORERS are the most damaging pests of peaches. The larvae winter in burrows in the tree trunk, from a foot above the surface to just beneath the soil level. When full grown, the caterpillars change into pupae, spinning a silken cocoon mixed with their excrement and gum from the tree. Adult moths emerge during summer and early fall. Unlike most moths, they fly by day. The females lay their eggs on the trunk of trees, commonly on injured or previously infested trees. The larvae bore immediately into the bark and begin feeding. If an infestation is not stopped, the tree dies. Simple controls are effective, however. The trunk of the tree can be sprayed with a contact insecticide. Or crystals of paradichlorobenzene spread in a circle around the base of the tree trunk and covered lightly with soil will give off a gas and kill young borers in their burrows. Consult an agricultural agent for the best time to apply controls.

LESSER PEACH TREE BORERS are similar to the Peach Tree Borer in appearance and in type of damage, though they generally attack higher on the trunk or in large branches. To control these pests, injured parts of tree must be sprayed in the fall, after the eggs have hatched. Larvae can also be dug out with a knife, as can Peach Tree Borers.

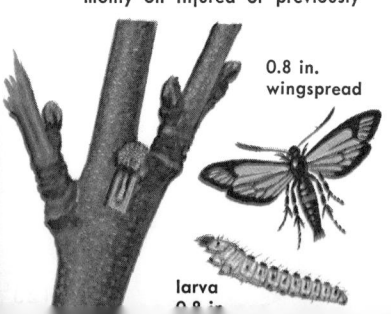

0.8 in.
wingspread

larva
0.8 in.

PEACH TWIG BORERS feed on the new growth of peach twigs, causing them to wilt and die. If a twig dies before a larva completes its growth, the larva moves to another twig. When about half an inch long, the larva spins a cocoon on the branch of a tree and transforms into a moth. Females lay eggs on twigs. As many as four generations are produced in a season, the later generations also attacking fruit. Apply a lime-sulfur or oil-emulsion spray to infested trees to kill larvae in cocoons. Check with your local agricultural agent.

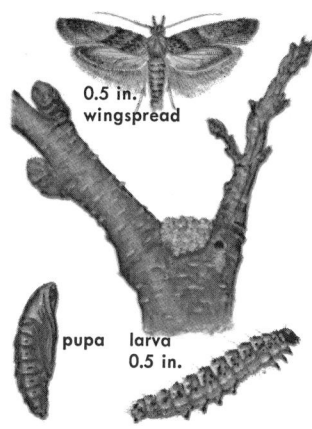

0.5 in. wingspread

pupa   larva 0.5 in.

ORIENTAL FRUIT MOTHS, closely related to the Codling Moth, are pests principally of peaches but also attack apples, plums, pears, and other fruits. The full-grown larvae overwinter in silken cocoons attached to the bark of the tree or in debris on the ground. They transform into pupae and emerge as adult moths in the spring. In a few days the females lay their eggs on leaves or twigs. The larvae of the first generation feed on the young twigs, causing them to die. In about a month the larvae are full grown. They spin cocoons, pupate, and emerge as adults about a week later. In the South there are as many as seven generations a year; in the North, four. Later generations feed inside the fruit. Oriental Fruit Moths are controlled to some degree by an introduced wasp that parasitizes the caterpillars. Many overwintering larvae can be killed by cultivating the orchard in the spring. Apply contact insecticides to the trees approximately every three weeks.

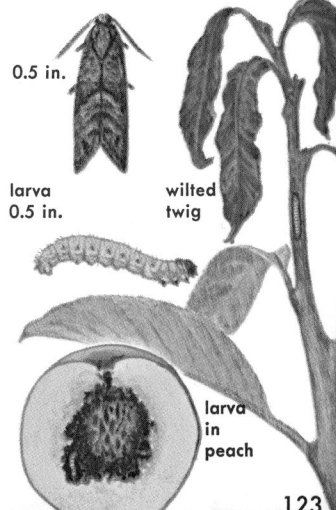

0.5 in.

larva 0.5 in.

wilted twig

larva in peach

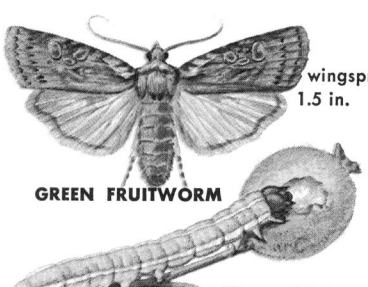

wingspread, 1.5 in.

caterpillar 0.4 in.

in cherry

GREEN FRUITWORM

CHERRY FRUITWORM

caterpillar, to 1.3 in., feeding on young apple

wingspread, 0.5 in.

FRUITWORMS The Green Fruitworm, though seldom abundant, feeds on apples and other fruits or on tender foliage and buds. The larvae, usually full grown by June, crawl down the tree and transform into the pupal stage in a silken cocoon in the soil. The adult moths emerge in late summer or fall and hibernate in winter. They die the following spring after mating and laying eggs. The worms can be killed with contact insecticides applied in early spring before the buds have opened. The Green Fruitworm occurs in eastern U.S.; the Cherry Fruitworm, similar in habits, mainly in the Northwest. Cherry Fruitworm larvae feed inside cherries until full grown. They hibernate under the bark and transform into pupae in the spring. Adult moths emerge in early summer, and females lay their eggs on developing fruit. Trees should be sprayed with a contact insecticide at this time.

FRUIT-TREE LEAF ROLLER

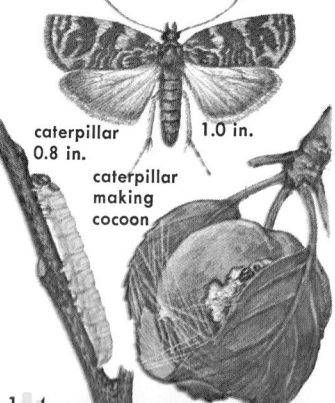

caterpillar 0.8 in.

1.0 in.

caterpillar making cocoon

LEAF ROLLERS eat leaves, green twigs, and buds, injuring many kinds of trees and shrubs (p. 93). Species that attack fruit trees feed on the developing fruit. Fruit-tree Leaf Roller caterpillars hatch in the spring from eggs laid on the bark or twigs the previous fall. They pupate in a roll of leaves held together with silk. The adult moths emerge in midsummer, and within a few days the females lay eggs. The most successful control is obtained with the use of an oil-spray insecticide applied to each of the brownish egg masses on the bark or twigs.

WEEVILS that damage fruit or fruit trees do so both as adult beetles and as larvae, or grubs. Many kinds of weevils are pests also of vegetables (p. 78), field and forage crops (p. 105), and stored products (p. 146).

PLUM CURCULIOS are pests of apples, cherries, peaches, plums, and other stone fruits. Adults hibernate beneath trash under trees and in early spring feed on buds and young leaves. The female chews a hole in a developing fruit, then lays an egg inside. The beetle uses her snout to push the egg deep into the hole. Finally she cuts a crescent-shaped slit in the skin of the fruit below where the egg is laid. Hundreds of eggs may be laid in one fruit; the spots and crescents are a telltale sign of an infestation. The eggs hatch in about a week, and the grubs burrow into flesh toward the stone or seeds, around which they feed. The fruit usually drops before the larvae are full grown. When the larvae reach full growth, they emerge and burrow into the soil to pupate. Adults appear in midsummer and feed on fruit on the ground until cold weather, when they hibernate. Orchards should be cleaned of trash under which the adults might hibernate. Plow or disk the orchard in early summer to kill the pupae. Destroy any dropped fruit. Spray the trees with a contact insecticide after they have bloomed.

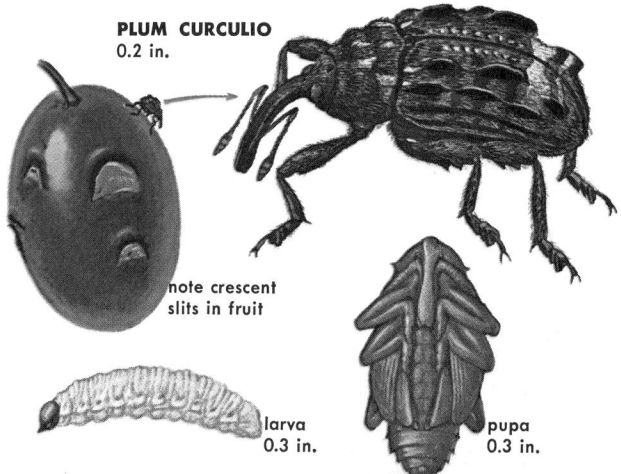

PLUM CURCULIO
0.2 in.

note crescent slits in fruit

larva
0.3 in.

pupa
0.3 in.

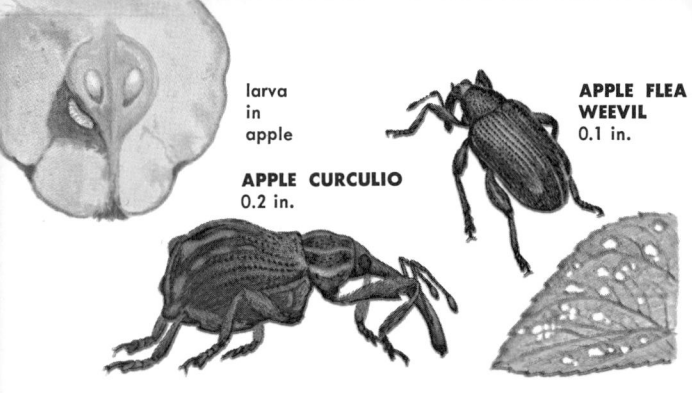

larva
in
apple

APPLE FLEA WEEVIL
0.1 in.

APPLE CURCULIO
0.2 in.

APPLE CURCULIOS are similar to Plum Curculios in the damage they do to fruit. The Apple Curculio has a much longer snout and a broader body. Females do not make crescent-shaped scars on the fruit when they lay eggs, and the larvae pupate inside the fruit. The fruit becomes stunted, knotty, and mummified. In heavy infestations fruit drops before ripening. Adults emerge in midsummer and feed until cold weather, then hibernate under debris until spring. Best control is a thorough cleanup of the orchard when an infestation is discovered. Chemical controls are difficult, as beetles feed deep in fruit. A variety of the Apple Curculio attacks cherries.

APPLE FLEA WEEVILS are pests mainly in the Midwest. Adults feed on buds and young leaves in the spring. The grub, or larva, mines through the leaf tissues. At the edge of the leaf the larva forms a blister-like cell in which it transforms into the pupa. Adult beetles appear in late May or June, feed on the foliage for a few weeks, and then become inactive through the summer. They hibernate in winter and begin feeding again in early spring. Contact insecticides applied beneath the trees will kill many of the hibernating adults in the fall, or trees can be sprayed in early spring. Check with your agricultural agent for the best time for spraying locally.

IMBRICATED SNOUT BEETLE

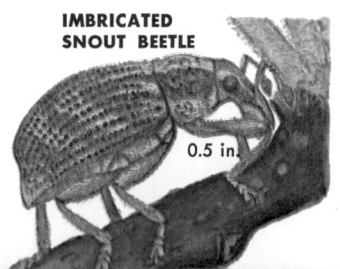

0.5 in.

IMBRICATED SNOUT BEETLES eat buds, young fruit, and leaves of apples and other fruit trees. Adults appear in June, feed for several weeks, then become inactive until spring. The larvae feed in roots of legumes and other plants. Control is by the same methods used for Apple Flea Weevil.

BORERS that feed on the inner bark and sapwood of fruit and shade trees are the grubs, or larvae, of beetles. Usually they attack only the young or injured and already weakened trees.

0.6 in.

ROUNDHEADED APPLE TREE BORER 0.9 in.

ROUNDHEADED APPLE TREE BORERS burrow into apple, pear, and other trees. The soft-bodied grubs have an enlarged, round area just behind their head and make round tunnels. Small trees are girdled and killed. Two (sometimes three) winters are spent as grubs. Full-grown grubs pupate in spring, and adults emerge in early summer. They feed on leaves and twigs but do little damage. Females lay eggs in slits cut in bark at base of trunk. Young grubs usually work near soil line; older grubs feed higher, bore deeper. Dig grubs from burrows with knife or wire probe or fumigate burrows. Contact insecticides kill adults.

FLATHEADED APPLE TREE BORERS attack nearly all kinds of trees and shrubs. The grubs burrow through the inner bark and sapwood and are especially damaging to young trees. The grubs, which work mainly on the sunny side of the tree, have a flattened enlargement just behind the head. The grubs hibernate in their burrows, which are filled with excrement and sawdust. They form pupae in the spring and emerge in early summer. Like the larvae, the adult beetles congregate on the sunny side of the tree, the females laying their eggs in cracks in the bark. The trunks of young trees should be wrapped in paper or cloth. Borers can be dug out.

grub to 1.2 in.

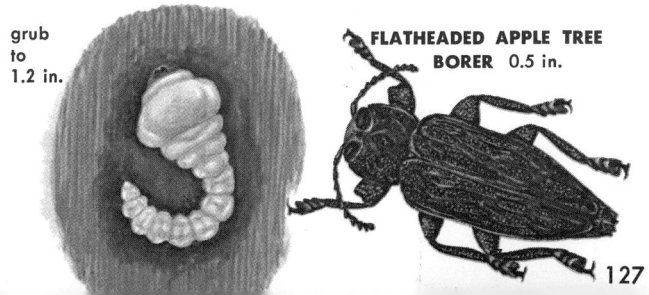

FLATHEADED APPLE TREE BORER 0.5 in.

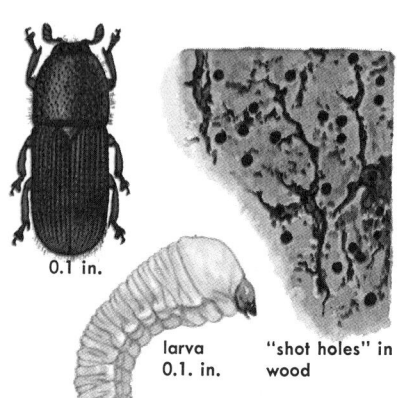

0.1 in.

larva
0.1. in.

"shot holes" in wood

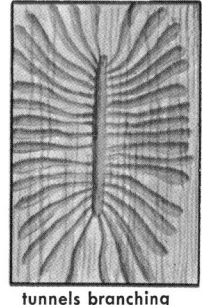

tunnels branching from parent gallery

SHOT-HOLE BORER

SHOT-HOLE BORERS tunnel in the inner bark of fruit and shade trees. The grub tunnels are branches from a parent gallery, about two inches long, in which the female beetle laid her eggs. When full grown the grubs form pupae at the end of the tunnel, and the adults bore straight out through the bark, making the identifying "shot holes." The adult beetles fly from tree to tree. Females usually lay eggs in an already injured tree. The leaves of an infested branch turn yellow and drop; small trees are killed. Infested trees should be sprayed with a contact insecticide in late spring, when the adults are emerging, or in the fall, when the adults are laying eggs. Healthy trees are seldom attacked, as the females cannot find places to enter to lay eggs. The beetles overwinter in the grub stage.

larva
0.1 in.

PEACH BARK BEETLE

0.1 in.
parent gallery and tunnels

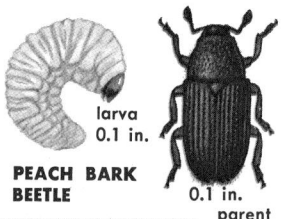

PEACH BARK BEETLES are closely related to the Shot-hole Borer and their damage is similar. The parent gallery runs across the grain of the trunk; the Shot-hole Borer's gallery runs with the grain. Peach Bark Beetle grubs tunnel with the grain; Shot-hole Borer grubs work across the grain. Peach Bark Beetles are controlled by the same methods used for the Shot-hole Borer.

SINUATE PEAR TREE BORER

0.3 in.

full-grown grub
0.5 to 1.5 in.

SINUATE PEAR TREE BORERS tunnel through the inner bark of pear, hawthorn, and other trees. The larvae, or grubs, hibernate in the burrows, which cause the bark of the tree to split and darken. Full-grown grubs pupate in the spring and emerge in early summer as adults. The beetles feed on the foliage but do little damage at this stage. The females lay their eggs in cracks in the bark, and the grubs bore inside. Two years are required to complete a life cycle. Young trees are commonly killed. Dead or infested limbs should be cut off and destroyed. Trees should be sprayed twice —late May and early June.

JAPANESE BEETLES feed on the foliage of many kinds of shade and fruit trees and also destroy fruit. Many beetles congregate on one plant. The grubs are major pests in lawns and greens, feeding on grass roots. In most areas two years are spent as grubs. The larvae then pupate in the soil, emerging as adults in midsummer. Adults are killed with contact-insecticide sprays or lured to traps. Grubs are killed by treating the soil with insecticides and also with ''milky spore'' (p. 13).

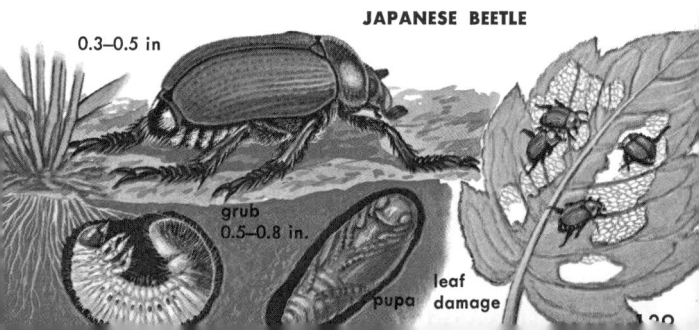

JAPANESE BEETLE

0.3–0.5 in

grub
0.5–0.8 in.

pupa

leaf
damage

MAGGOTS, the larvae of flies, are sometimes serious pests of fruits. Maggots feed deep inside fruit; hence to be effective controls must be applied when the adults are laying eggs.

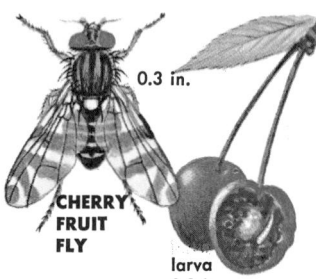

CHERRY FRUIT FLY

larva
0.3 in.

0.3 in.

CHERRY FRUIT FLIES infest pears, plums, and other fruits as well as cherries. The maggots hatch from eggs laid in slits cut in the fruit by the female flies. They feed on the flesh of the fruit and cause it to be dwarfed, misshapen, or decayed. When full grown, the worms drop to the ground and pupate in loose soil or under debris. Adults emerge late the following spring and feed on leaves or developing fruit by scraping surface and sucking juices. Stomach-poison or contact insecticides, applied in spring are effective.

APPLE MAGGOTS tunnel through apples, blueberries, and other fruits, reducing the flesh to a brown, decaying pulp. When full grown—and usually after the fruit has dropped—the maggots emerge and pupate in debris or in loose soil. Adults appear in late June or July the following summer. In about ten days the females lay their eggs in fruit, puncturing the skin with their sharp ovipositor. Lead arsenate or contact insecticides are effective. An agricultural agent can advise best time to spray.

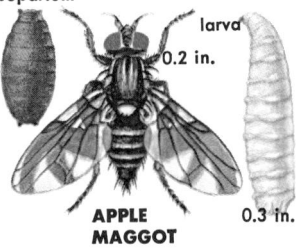

puparium

larva

0.2 in.

0.3 in.

APPLE MAGGOT

MEDITERRANEAN FRUIT FLY larvae feed on citrus fruits, peaches, plums, and other fleshy fruits. This dangerous pest has gained entry to continental U.S. several times through introductions in Florida, but each time has been exterminated. Mexican Fruit Fly has been kept in check by inspection and control along Texas-Mexico border.

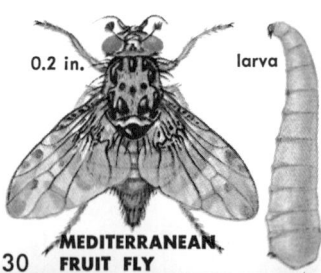

0.2 in.

larva

MEDITERRANEAN FRUIT FLY

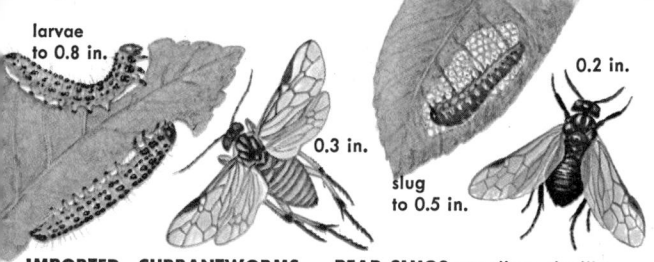

larvae
to 0.8 in.

0.3 in.

slug
to 0.5 in.

0.2 in.

IMPORTED CURRANTWORMS hatch from eggs laid on the leaves of currant or gooseberry bushes. The larvae eat from margin of leaf toward center. When full grown, they drop to the ground to pupate. In warm regions there are two and a partial third generation every year.

PEAR SLUGS are slimy, sluglike larvae that eat the foliage of pears, plums, cherries, and other fruit trees. Only the veins of the leaves remain. The full-grown worms pupate in the soil. A second generation appears in midsummer, in heavy infestations completely defoliating trees.

SAWFLY LARVAE are leaf feeders (p. 95) attacking many plants. They are easily killed with stomach-poison or contact insecticides.

APHIDS, or plant lice, are all similar in habits and life history, which is often complex (p. 66). All are injurious pests of plants, and some species are especially injurious to fruits.

WOOLLY APPLE APHIDS secrete a woolly, white wax over their body as they feed. They overwinter either in the egg stage in crevices on the bark of elms or as nymphs hibernating on roots of apple trees. Nymphs that hatch from the eggs on elms feed on the leaves and buds. In the third generation winged forms appear and migrate to apple trees, where they feed on roots, causing galls to form. Sometimes they stay on the roots for two seasons, through several generations. They stunt the tree's growth and may kill it. These pests are difficult to control. Stomach-poison or contact insecticides are effective if applied heavily. An introduced wasp parasite is also effective.

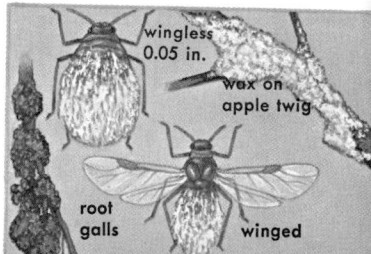

wingless
0.05 in.

wax on
apple twig

root
galls

winged

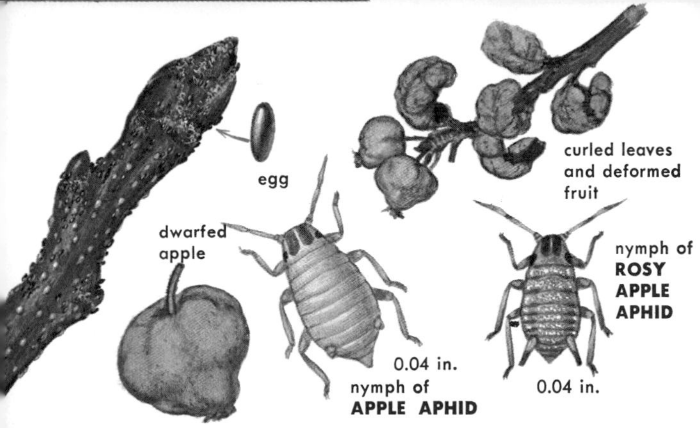

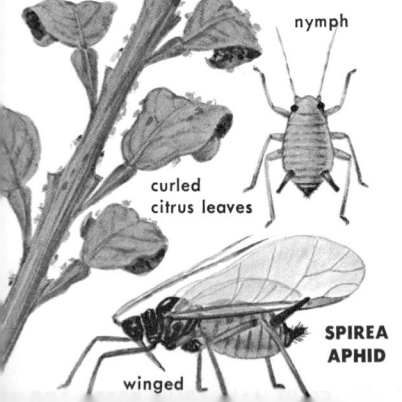

egg

curled leaves
and deformed
fruit

dwarfed
apple

0.04 in.
nymph of
APPLE APHID

nymph of
**ROSY
APPLE
APHID**

0.04 in.

APPLE APHIDS overwinter as eggs on the bark of trees. Nymphs hatch in early spring and feed first on buds. A contact insecticide applied at this time gives good control, especially since all of the eggs hatch at about the same time. Trees can be sprayed a second time in late summer to kill winged adults that may have migrated from nearby orchards or from wild host trees.

ROSY APPLE APHIDS are pests principally of apples but may also infest pears, hawthorns, and such nonwoody plants as plantains. Leaves and twigs of an infested tree curl and the fruit becomes hard and knotty. The eggs hatch over a period of several weeks in early spring about the time the trees begin to bud. Dormant oil sprays (p. 22) will destroy both the eggs and newly hatched nymphs.

nymph

curled
citrus leaves

**SPIREA
APHID**

winged

SPIREA APHIDS collect in large numbers on the new growth of spirea and other plants. Also known as the Green Citrus Aphid, this species commonly attacks citrus in Florida and California. It causes leaves to curl, deforms fruit, and covers the ground with honeydew, on which black sooty mold grows. It also transmits a virus disease. Winged forms, produced whenever a colony becomes crowded, migrate to other trees. Use contact insecticide sprays in early spring, before the population of aphids has built up.

SCALES AND MEALYBUGS are so modified in body form that they are often not recognized as insects (p. 86). All of the thousands of species damage plants by feeding on their juices, thus stunting their growth and deforming the fruit. Scales and mealybugs are the most destructive insect pests of citrus.

CALIFORNIA RED SCALE is the most damaging scale pest of citrus in California, occurring less abundantly in Texas, Arizona, and the Gulf states. California Red Scale is also a pest of many other fruit trees and ornamentals. It feeds on the stems and leaves as well as on the fruit. Nymphs crawl over the plant for several hours before settling to feed and secreting a waxy covering over their body. Males mature in about two months and emerge from scale as yellow-winged adults. Each inseminates an immobile female, then dies. Fertile females give birth to two or three young every day for several months. Four generations are produced every season. Trees are fumigated with hydrogen-cyanide gas or are sprayed with a contact insecticide to kill the "crawler" nymphs.

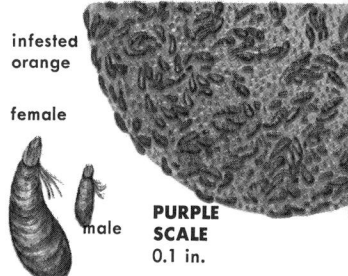

infested orange

female

male

PURPLE SCALE
0.1 in.

PURPLE SCALE, a widely distributed species, is the most damaging citrus scale pest in Florida. It also occurs in California. In addition to citrus, this scale infests avocados, pecans, and many ornamentals. In Florida, controlled by spraying with oil to kill the young still crawling and before they secrete a protective armor. Parathion and other contact insecticides are used in California.

CALIFORNIA RED SCALE

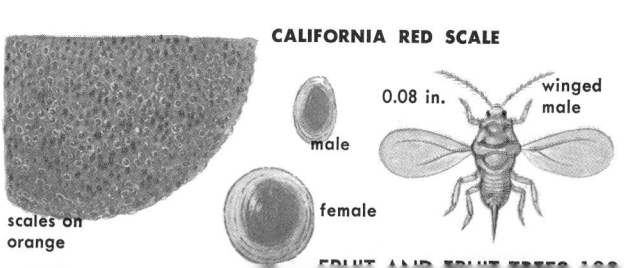

scales on orange

male

0.08 in.

winged male

female

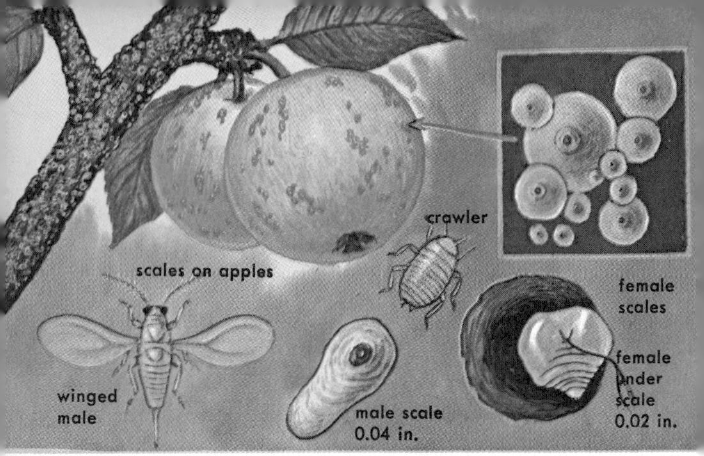

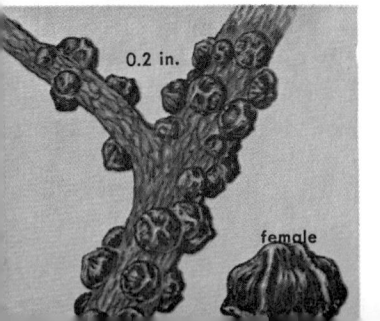

scales on apples

crawler

winged male

male scale 0.04 in.

female scales

female under scale 0.02 in.

SAN JOSE SCALE is damaging to apple, pear, peach, cherry, and many other fruit and shade trees and ornamental plants. Heavy infestations may kill the trees, which are first weakened and their foliage yellowed. Infested fruit is spotted. San José Scales overwinter as partly grown nymphs, or crawlers, that cling to the bark of the tree. They begin to feed in early spring, as soon as the sap starts to flow, and are full grown by the time the trees bloom. The winged males inseminate the females, which never emerge from under their scale. Females give birth to as many as 500 nymphs in 1½ months. The tiny mitelike crawlers move over the plant for several hours before settling to feed, secreting a waxy scale over themselves. In the crawling stage they may be blown by the wind or carried by man or other animals to infest other plants. As many as six generations are produced each year. A dormant spray in late winter or early spring kills overwintering nymphs. Wasp parasites also effective.

BLACK SCALE infests citrus, apples, figs, grapes, pears, and many ornamentals in warm regions and is also a greenhouse pest in cold climates. In addition to the damage done by sucking the plant's juices, large amounts of honeydew are excreted on which sooty mold grows. Controlled principally with oil sprays. An introduced wasp parasite is also effective.

0.2 in.

female

COTTONY-CUSHION SCALES are pests of citrus and many other fruit trees and ornamentals. The female, which has a brown or reddish body, secretes a large cottony mass containing as many as 1,000 red eggs. Both the young and the adults can move, although the female stops moving after her egg sac forms. The tiny males are winged.

Cottony-cushion Scale, once the most damaging pest of citrus in California, was brought under control by Vedalia, a predatory lady beetle introduced from Australia. The use of insecticides to kill other pests has destroyed the Vedalia in some areas, where insecticides must be used now to control the Cottony-cushion Scale until the beetles are again established.

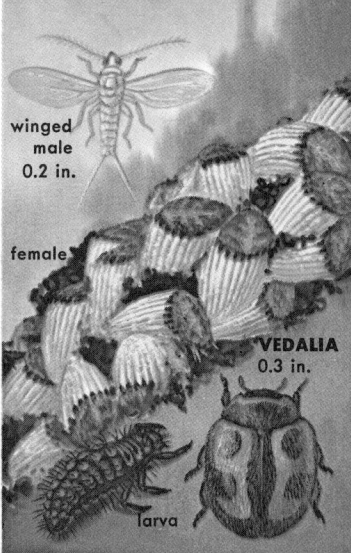

winged male 0.2 in.

female

VEDALIA 0.3 in.

larva

CITRUS MEALYBUGS suck the juices from the leaves, stems, and fruit of citrus and many other plants. In warm climates they are outdoor pests, sometimes infesting potatoes and vegetable crops. In cool climates they are pests of house plants and in greenhouses. Citrus Mealybugs expel large amounts of honeydew. Females are covered with wax; males are winged. On small plants they can be picked off by hand, washed off with water, or killed with contact insecticides. In groves lady beetles and parasitic wasps have been effective controls for Citrus and related Citrophilus, Grape, and Long-tailed mealybugs.

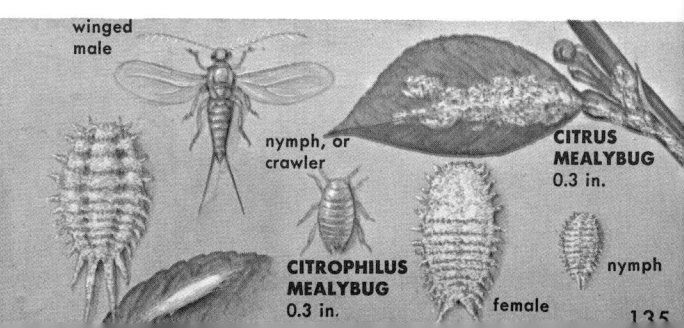

winged male

nymph, or crawler

CITRUS MEALYBUG 0.3 in.

CITROPHILUS MEALYBUG 0.3 in.

female

nymph

135

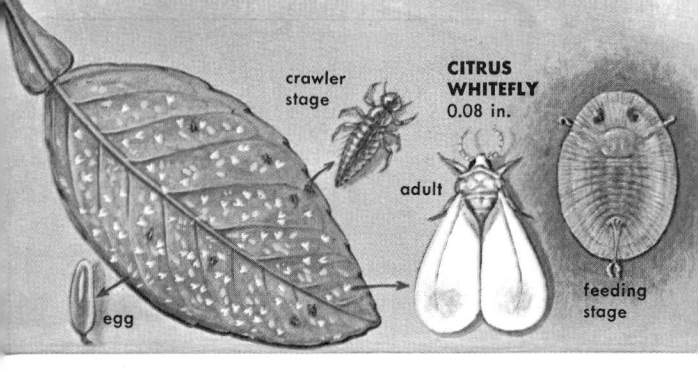

crawler
stage

**CITRUS
WHITEFLY**
0.08 in.

adult

egg

feeding
stage

WHITEFLIES are tiny insects in a family closely related to aphids and scale insects. Two dozen or so species, including the Greenhouse Whitefly (p. 88), are damaging to ornamentals and fruit trees, particularly citrus and other plants that grow in warm climates. Fruit on an infested tree is discolored by sooty mold. If an infestation is allowed to persist, the plant's growth is stunted and its yield is greatly reduced. All whiteflies have a similar life history. The female lays her eggs on short stalks attached to the underside of leaves. The nymphs hatch in 4–12 days and are called "crawlers" because they move about over the plant. Soon, however, they insert their beaks into a stem or leaf and begin to feed on the plant's juices. When the nymphs shed, they lose their legs and their antennae are greatly reduced in size. At this stage the nymphs are immobile and resemble scales. On the fourth molt the adults emerge. Both males and females are winged and are covered with white, powdery scales. As many as three or four generations are produced in a season in warm climates. Infested plants should be sprayed in spring and fall with an oil emulsion or with a contact insecticide, such as malathion or parathion. Consult local agricultural agent for best time to spray.

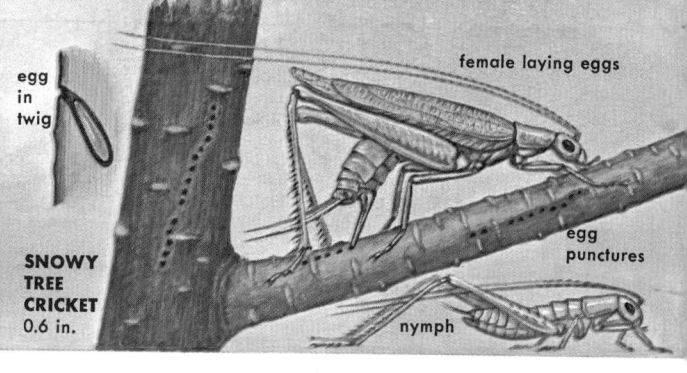

egg
in
twig

female laying eggs

egg
punctures

**SNOWY
TREE
CRICKET**
0.6 in.

nymph

TREE CRICKETS lay eggs in the branches or stems of trees and shrubs. The female drills a hole, lays an egg, then moves forward and repeats the process, sometimes laying several dozen eggs in a row. The stem beyond the punctures usually dies. Spray with lead arsenate or other stomach poison in summer before egg laying begins. Remove and burn punctured stems in the fall.

CITRUS THRIPS is a serious pest in California but does not occur in Florida. It feeds on buds, new growth and young fruit, scraping away outer tissues and sucking up juices. Infested trees grow slowly and fruit shows distinct ring scar. Thrips winter in the egg stage on leaves and stems. A life cycle is completed in about three weeks or less. Both stomach-poison and contact insecticides are effective.

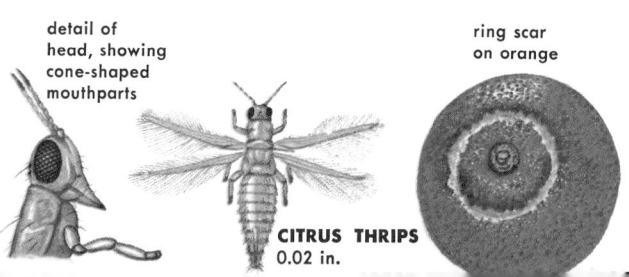

detail of
head, showing
cone-shaped
mouthparts

ring scar
on orange

CITRUS THRIPS
0.02 in.

egg, with
stalk and
silk guys

0.002 in.
male

CITRUS RED MITES, called Purple Mites in Florida, cause the leaves of infested trees to be speckled, finally turning brown and dropping. The fruit is discolored. The Citrus Red Mite is an especially serious pest in California. Six-spotted Mites are more abundant in Florida. They collect on underside of leaves.

MITES, relatives of spiders and ticks, have become more serious pests in recent years. Some of the newer insecticides kill the predators and parasites of mites. Only those mites especially damaging to citrus are described here. Other pests include the European Red Mite, Pacific Spider Mite, and Pear Leaf Blister Mite, which infest pear, cherry, apple, and other fruit trees of temperate regions. Mites are also pests of man (p. 45), domestic animals and pets (pp. 54–55), vegetable crops (p. 85), and flowers and shrubs (p. 90). Oil sprays, sulfur dusts, and lime-sulfur sprays are effective controls, as are special miticides. Your agricultural agent can tell you the best chemical and time of application in your area.

CITRUS BUD MITES, pests mainly in California, feed on buds and blossoms of lemons, less commonly on other citrus. Fruit leaves and twigs are deformed.

CITRUS RUST MITES, serious pests in Florida, damage mainly oranges but also injure grapefruit, limes, and lemons. Females lay eggs on fruit and leaves.

0.006 in.

0.006 in.

PESTS OF FOREST AND SHADE TREES

Insect pests destroy more timber than do forest fires. Ordinarily the damage is not conspicuous, but in severe outbreaks whole stands of timber may be killed in one season. Some species spread plant diseases. State and national government agencies battle forest insects in large-scale control programs.

BEETLES are damaging to trees both as adults and as larvae (grubs). Most injurious are the borers that work in the wood of the trunk or in the branches.

SMALLER EUROPEAN ELM BARK BEETLE

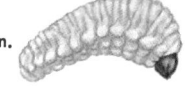

grub
to 0.3 in.

0.2 in.

ELM BARK BEETLES are carriers of the deadly Dutch elm disease, caused by a fungus. The Smaller European Elm Bark Beetle was introduced to North America in 1909, the disease in 1930. The Native Elm Bark Beetle is now also a carrier. Adults of both species appear in late spring or early summer and feed on branches or twigs. Eggs are laid only in dead or dying wood. Keeping trees healthy and eliminating damaged or diseased portions gives partial control.

ELM LEAF BEETLES overwinter as adults and in early spring lay clusters of eggs on underside of elm leaves. Grubs and adults feed on leaves. Grubs are full grown in about three weeks. They pupate in debris under tree and emerge as adults in about two weeks. Three or more generations are completed in a year. Spray leaves with stomach-poison or contact insecticides to destroy grubs and adults, and at base of infested tree to kill grubs descending to pupate.

ELM LEAF BEETLE

grub
0.5. in.

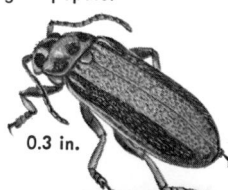

0.3 in.

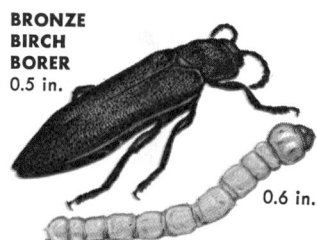

BRONZE BIRCH BORER
0.5 in.

0.6 in.

BRONZE BIRCH BORERS are mainly injurious to birches but may also attack willows, poplars, and cottonwoods. The larvae overwinter in the sapwood, forming pupae in early spring and emerging as adults in late spring or early summer. Females lay their eggs in crevices in the bark. On hatching, the grubs immediately burrow into the wood. Their tunnels, sometimes 4 feet long, may cut off the flow of sap. First the tips of the branches turn brown, then the tree dies. The Bronze Birch Borer, related to the Flatheaded Apple Tree Borer (p. 127), is most likely to attack sick or injured trees. Use contact insecticides for adults.

LOCUST BORERS winter as small larvae in the bark and start their tunneling into the wood in spring, causing swollen areas to appear on the trunk. The borers commonly kill the tree. Full-grown grubs pupate in cells in the wood in midsummer. Adult beetles appear in late summer or early fall. They fly actively, feeding on flowers. The females lay their eggs in cracks in bark, most often attacking small or weakened trees. Spray trunks with a contact insecticide before tree starts spring growth.

POPLAR BORERS are long-horned beetles. The grubs tunnel in the trunk and large limbs of trees, weakening the wood so that limbs break off. Eventually an infested tree dies. Larvae are usually full grown in two years but may take three years to complete development. They pupate in the burrows and emerge as adults in late summer or early fall. The female beetle deposits eggs in cracks in the bark. The newly hatched grubs immediately burrow inside. Larvae can be killed with probes or by fumigating tunnels with carbon bisulfide (see Roundheaded Apple Tree Borer, p. 127). Badly infested trees should be cut and burned to prevent spread.

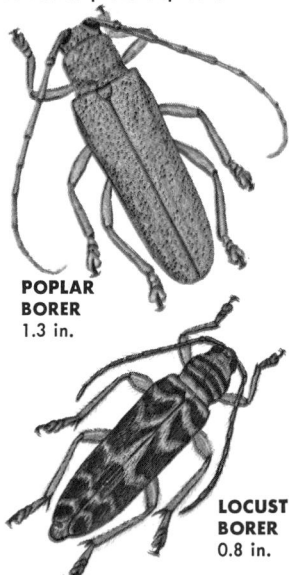

POPLAR BORER
1.3 in.

LOCUST BORER
0.8 in.

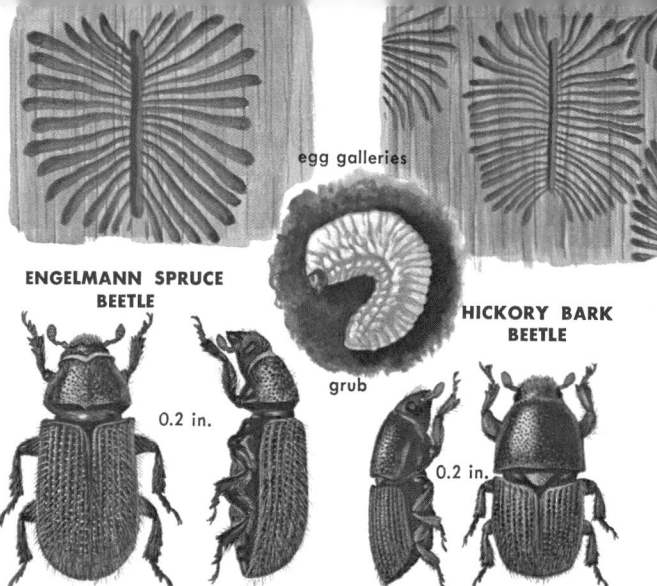

egg galleries

ENGELMANN SPRUCE BEETLE

grub

HICKORY BARK BEETLE

0.2 in.

0.2 in.

ENGELMANN SPRUCE BEETLES bore through the outer bark of living trees, cutting egg galleries parallel to the surface. Each gallery contains about 125 eggs. The grubs feed on the wood near the chamber until cold weather, rest until spring, then feed again. They pupate in midsummer and become adults in late summer or fall, spending the winter under the bark of the girdled and dying or dead trees. The following spring the beetles infest new trees. Normally the beetles are controlled by natural predators. Foresters check constantly for infestations. Bark of infested trees is peeled off and burned, or trees treated with a penetrating insecticide.

BARK BEETLES of several species damage conifers, and less commonly, deciduous trees. Among these are the Hickory Bark Beetle, Douglas Fir Engraver, Western Pine Beetle, and Southern Pine Beetle. Typically the beetles mine, or tunnel, just beneath bark to make galleries for eggs. More extensive tunnels ramify from galleries as the grubs feed. Sap occasionally flows from tunnels, and dust of borings collects around base of tree. Tunnels open way for fungus diseases, and destruction of cambium eventually kills tree. In street and yard plantings, prune dead wood of trees to destroy breeding places. Kill adults with contact insecticide.

CATERPILLARS, the larvae of moths and butterflies, feed on the leaves, buds, and flowers of many kinds of trees and shrubs. Certain species of moths are among the most damaging pests of forests. Control of the most serious pests may involve several states or an entire region. Such large-scale control programs are conducted by state and federal agencies. Infestations of shade trees may be controlled locally.

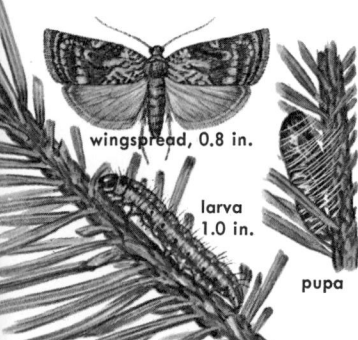

wingspread, 0.8 in.

larva 1.0 in.

pupa

SPRUCE BUDWORM

SPRUCE BUDWORMS, of the conifer forests of eastern United States and Canada, are among the most injurious of all insect pests. Young caterpillars overwinter beneath bark and become active in early spring, feeding on buds and new growth. They are full grown by early summer, forming pupae and transforming into adults. Moths lay eggs in late summer. Heavy infestations kill trees; light infestations turn needles brown. Control with stomach-poison or contact insecticides.

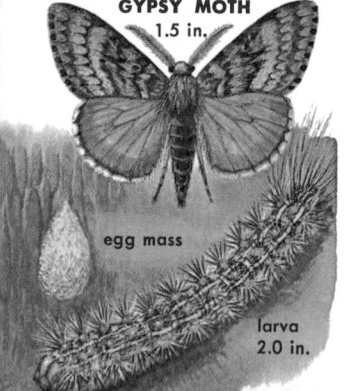

GYPSY MOTH
1.5 in.

egg mass

larva 2.0 in.

GYPSY MOTH caterpillars feed on leaves of deciduous trees, conifers, and many other plants. They form pupae in midsummer and emerge as adults in July and August. The Gypsy Moth overwinters in the egg stage. As the females cannot fly well, the Gypsy Moth is spread long distances principally by man—on cars, trucks, trains, or other vehicles. The caterpillars spin silken threads and may be blown by the wind. Egg masses can be destroyed or the trunks of trees treated with a contact insecticide to kill caterpillars.

FOREST TENT CATERPILLARS at times migrate in armies of millions, defoliating trees and shrubs in their path. They usually feed on the leaves of oaks, maples, elms, ash, and conifers. Winter is passed in the egg stage, and the larvae hatch in early spring. Adult moths appear in midsummer. Forest Tent Caterpillars, despite their name, do not make tents, as do the closely related Eastern Tent Caterpillars. Foliage of infested trees can be sprayed with a stomach-poison or contact insecticide to kill caterpillars.

TUSSOCK MOTH caterpillars are hairy and usually have several long tufts of black hairs on the head and tail. The caterpillars hatch in late spring from egg masses laid on bark and leaves or on the cocoon case from which the nearly wingless females emerged. They feed on the foliage of a great variety of trees and shrubs and are full grown by midsummer. In many regions there are two generations a year. Egg masses can be painted with creosote or gathered and burned. The larvae can be killed with stomach-poison or contact insecticides. The White-marked Tussock Moth is a common and widespread species; others are the Hickory Tussock Moth, Douglas Fir Tussock Moth, and Western Tussock Moth. The Gypsy Moth (p. 142) and the Brown-tail Moth belong to the same family. The Brown-tail Moth, once a damaging pest in eastern United States, is now largely under control.

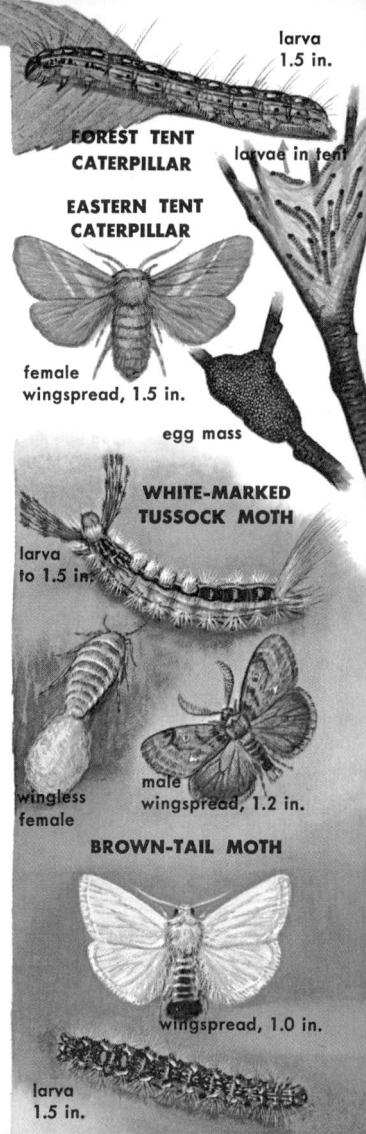

larva 1.5 in.

FOREST TENT CATERPILLAR

larvae in tent

EASTERN TENT CATERPILLAR

female wingspread, 1.5 in.

egg mass

WHITE-MARKED TUSSOCK MOTH

larva to 1.5 in.

wingless female

male wingspread, 1.2 in.

BROWN-TAIL MOTH

wingspread, 1.0 in.

larva 1.5 in.

CARPENTERWORM

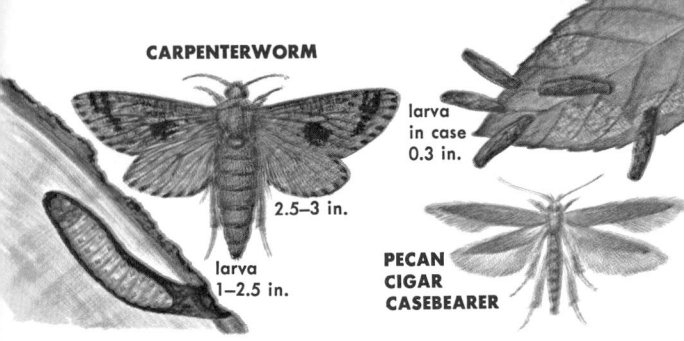

2.5–3 in.

larva
1–2.5 in.

larva
in case
0.3 in.

PECAN CIGAR CASEBEARER

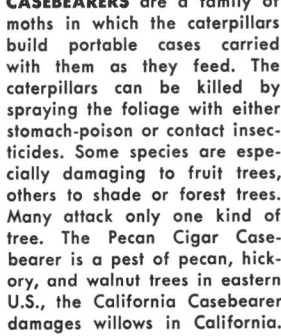

CARPENTERWORMS burrow into the wood of oaks, elms, maples, and other deciduous trees. The holes weaken the trees so that limbs break off in heavy winds. The damaged wood is greatly reduced in value. The full-grown larvae pupate in the wood. When it is time for the adults to emerge, the pupae wriggle their way partly out of the tree. The adult moth leaves the shed pupal skin in the hole. Each generation requires three years or longer. Best control is fumigation of burrows.

CASEBEARERS are a family of moths in which the caterpillars build portable cases carried with them as they feed. The caterpillars can be killed by spraying the foliage with either stomach-poison or contact insecticides. Some species are especially damaging to fruit trees, others to shade or forest trees. Many attack only one kind of tree. The Pecan Cigar Casebearer is a pest of pecan, hickory, and walnut trees in eastern U.S., the California Casebearer damages willows in California.

OAKWORMS are foliage feeders. The California Oakworm is a pest of live oaks in California. The Orange-striped Oakworm, of a different family, infests oaks of eastern U.S. Both will feed on other deciduous trees. In warm regions there may be two generations a year. Spray with stomach-poison or else with a contact insecticide.

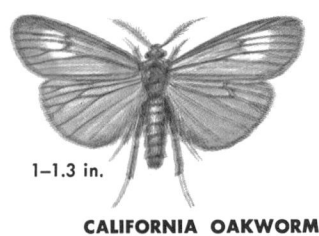

1–1.3 in.

CALIFORNIA OAKWORM

larva

chrysalid

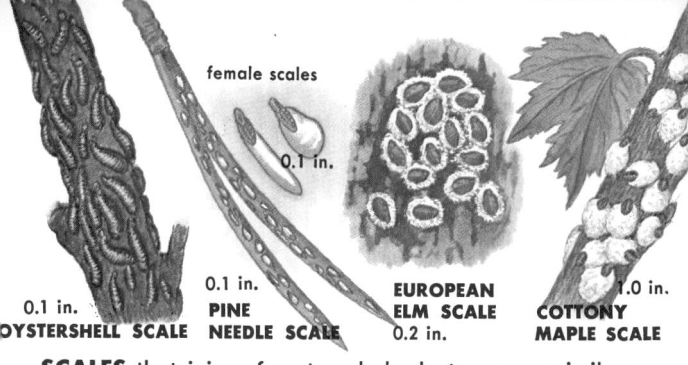

female scales
0.1 in.

0.1 in.
OYSTERSHELL SCALE

0.1 in.
PINE NEEDLE SCALE

EUROPEAN ELM SCALE
0.2 in.

1.0 in.
COTTONY MAPLE SCALE

SCALES that injure forest and shade trees are similar in life history to species damaging flowers and shrubs (p. 86) and citrus (p. 133). In heavy infestations the foliage turns brown and drops. Young plants may be killed. Oystershell, Pine Needle, Cottony Maple, and European Elm scales are common, widespread species. Scales are killed by applying a dormant oil spray before the plant buds in spring or by spraying with a contact insecticide when scales are in the crawling stage.

SAWFLY larvae look like caterpillars, though the adults belong to the same order of insects as bees, wasps, and ants. The larvae feed on foliage. Some species damage shade and forest trees. Kill larvae by spraying with either stomach-poison or contact insecticides when they are actively feeding.

0.1 in.

larva
1.5–1.8 in.

ELM SAWFLY

INSECT PESTS OF STORED PRODUCTS

Pest infestations in stored products are difficult to detect and control. The pests not only eat the grain or other stored products but may also create damp, warm conditions in which equally destructive molds can grow. Cheese, cured meats, furs, and wool fabrics are among the animal products attacked by insect pests. Other pests of stored products are described in the section on Household Pests (p. 24).

WEEVILS may destroy an entire storage of grain. Most damaging and widely distributed are Granary and the Rice weevils. The Granary Weevil does not fly, hence does not infest grain in the field. It thrives in northern climates; the Rice Weevil is most abundant in warm climates. The Rice Weevil can fly and often infests grain before storage. Adults of both species will eat whole grain or grain products. The larvae can develop only in whole kernels, in sizable pieces, or in flour that has become moist and caked. A life cycle is completed in one to two months, and the weevils overwinter either as larvae or as adults. Each female lays about 400 eggs in her lifetime. She chews a hole in a kernel and then deposits one egg inside. Adults live two years or longer and can survive long periods without food. In households, infested products should be burned, and the storage area cleaned thoroughly. Similar sanitary measures are taken in granaries, or the grain is fumigated.

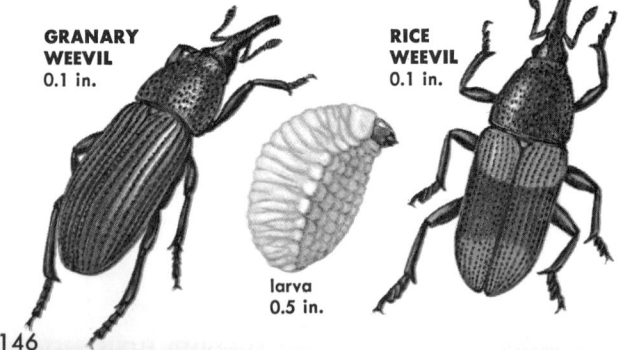

GRANARY WEEVIL
0.1 in.

RICE WEEVIL
0.1 in.

larva
0.5 in.

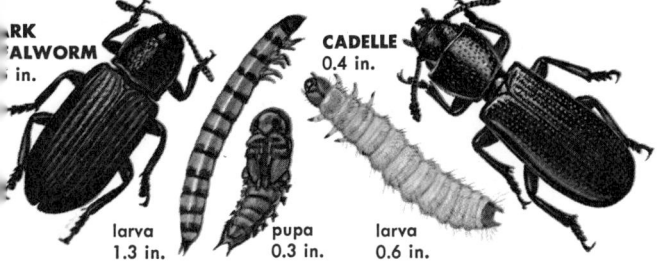

RK
ALWORM
in.

CADELLE
0.4 in.

larva
1.3 in.

pupa
0.3 in.

larva
0.6 in.

MEALWORMS feed on all types of grain and grain products, particularly if stored in dark, damp places. After six to nine months, larvae form pupae in grain and transform into adults. Yellow Mealworms are more abundant in cool climates, Dark Mealworms in warmer climates. In storage bins or elevators, larvae are killed by superheating, freezing, or fumigation.

FLOUR BEETLES feed on grain or grain products, spices, nuts, dried fruits, chocolate, and other stored foods. They give flour a disagreeable, moldy flavor. The Red Flour Beetle is most abundant in warm regions, the Confused Flour Beetle in cool climates. Both are worldwide in distribution and are among the most familiar of the stored-product pests to reach the home from the grocery store. Note

CADELLES are beetles that infest grains and seeds in storage. The larvae feed on the grain, but the adult beetles attack and eat other inescts or their larvae. Both the eggs and pupae are killed by low temperatures, but the adults and larvae survive long periods of cold. The adults and larvae tunnel into soft wood in storage areas and are most easily killed by fumigation.

that the Red Flour Beetle's antennae are enlarged abruptly, while the Confused Flour Beetle's antennae enlarge gradually. In the house, infested products should be destroyed and cupboards cleaned thoroughly. If a product must be saved, larvae can be killed if kept for several hours at 40 degrees F. or if heated to about 130 degrees F. for two hours. Destroying flour is usually most practical.

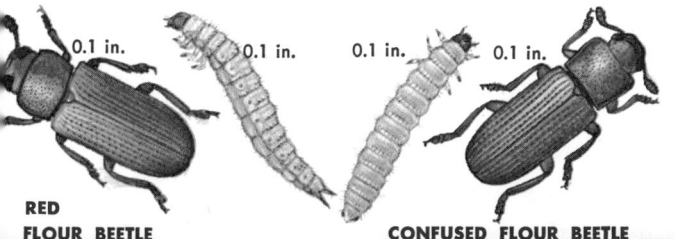

0.1 in.

0.1 in.

0.1 in.

0.1 in.

RED
FLOUR BEETLE

CONFUSED FLOUR BEETLE

SAW-TOOTHED GRAIN BEETLE

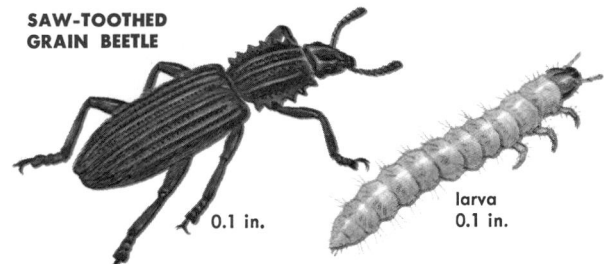

0.1 in.

larva
0.1 in.

SAW-TOOTHED GRAIN BEE-TLES, worldwide in distribution, feed on a wide variety of foods but especially on flour, cereals, and other grain products. The beetles are so flat they can crawl into sacks or boxes that appear to be tightly sealed. The females deposit their eggs in the food, and when full grown, the larvae form pupae and transform into adults. A life cycle usually takes about two months, with six or seven generations a year. All life stages are killed by cooling to 0 degrees F. for one day or heating to 125 degrees F. for an hour. Clean storage areas. Avoid contaminating foods with insecticides.

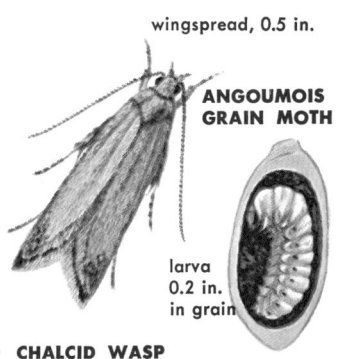

wingspread, 0.5 in.

ANGOUMOIS GRAIN MOTH

larva
0.2 in.
in grain

CHALCID WASP
0.02 in.

Parasitic wasp laying eggs in the egg of an Angoumois Moth

ANGOUMOIS GRAIN MOTH caterpillars attack grain in storage and also in the field. They prefer tender, damp grain rather than grain that is hard and dried. The larvae tunnel into the kernels and seal the entrance holes with silk. When full grown the larvae spin a cocoon in the cavity. If the seed is small, as in sorghums, several are tied together with silk, and the larva lives and feeds outside the seed in the silken ball. Life cycles are completed in about a month in warm weather. The larvae remain dormant in winter, prolonging life cycle to six months or more. Mills, bins, or warehouses are cleaned thoroughly, then pests killed by superheating, freezing, or fumigation. A tiny parasitic chalcid wasp is also an effective control.

LESSER GRAIN BORERS, pests of stored grains, particularly wheat, are damaging both as larvae and as adults. They also feed on wood and paper. The closely related Larger Grain Borer feeds mainly on corn and is a pest principally in southern United States. Both cold and heat, as used for the Sawtoothed Grain Beetle, are effective, as are fumigants for non-food substances.

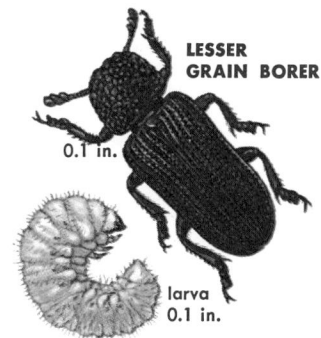

LESSER GRAIN BORER

0.1 in.

larva
0.1 in.

MEDITERRANEAN FLOUR MOTH caterpillars are especially serious pests in flour mills. The caterpillars spin a silken tube in which they live as they feed, and the web masses clog the machinery in the mills. In the home, the caterpillars are found in beans, dried fruits, and many other foods as well as in flour and grain products. As many as six generations may be completed in a year. Destroying the infested food material and cleaning storage areas are best home controls. In mills, pests are killed by fumigation.

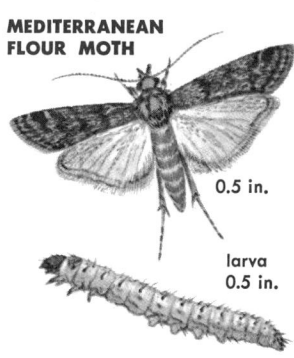

MEDITERRANEAN FLOUR MOTH

0.5 in.

larva
0.5 in.

INDIAN-MEAL MOTH caterpillars feed on a variety of stored foods, particularly dried fruits and cereals, spinning webs as they feed. In an abundance of food and with proper warmth and moisture a life cycle is completed in a month, with as many as six generations a year. Sanitation and continuous checking to catch infestations early are the best controls in the home. Bins, elevators, or other large storage areas are fumigated.

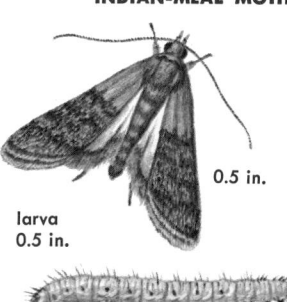

INDIAN-MEAL MOTH

0.5 in.

larva
0.5 in.

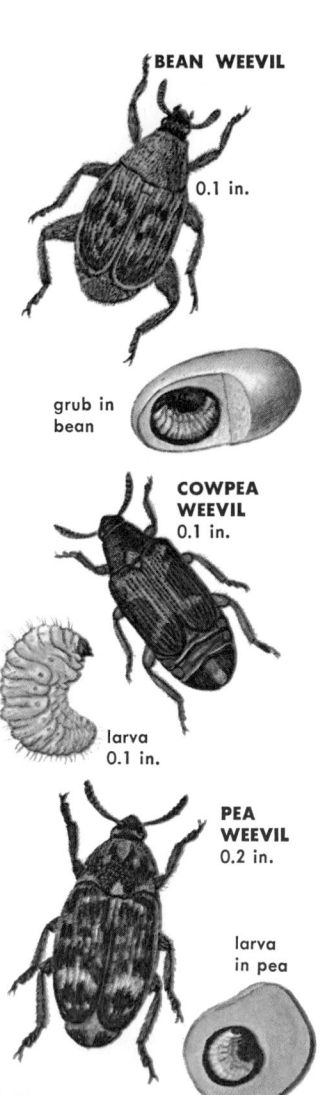

BEAN WEEVIL

0.1 in.

grub in bean

COWPEA WEEVIL
0.1 in.

larva
0.1 in.

PEA WEEVIL
0.2 in.

larva in pea

BEAN AND COWPEA WEEVILS eat out the center of stored beans, leaving only the shells. Bean Weevils are found throughout the U.S., the Cowpea Weevil most abundantly in southern states. The grubs, or larvae, hatch from eggs laid in holes chewed into stored beans or into pods in the field. In heavy infestations there may be two dozen or more tiny, newly hatched larvae in one bean. When full grown the larvae form pupae in the eaten-out cavity. As many as six generations are produced in a season. Infested beans should be destroyed. If the beans are to be planted rather than eaten, they should be fumigated first to kill the grubs. The larvae can also be killed by heating the seeds to 145 degrees F. for two hours. Bury vines and pods in the field.

PEA WEEVILS infest only peas. Adult beetles that overwinter in the field feed on the leaves and flowers of the pea plants in the spring. The female beetles lay their eggs on the pea pods, and the spiny larvae burrow inside and begin feeding on a developing seed. The entry hole made by the grub is sealed with silk. The full-grown grub forms a pupa in the seed and in about two weeks emerges as an adult. In cold climates adults may hibernate in stored peas and emerge in the spring. Vines, pods, and other debris should be buried. Plants can be sprayed with a contact insecticide when in bloom to kill adults, or peas can be fumigated at harvesting.

CIGARETTE BEETLE grubs feed on stored tobacco leaves and tobacco products. A life cycle is completed in about 1½ months, with as many as six generations a year. Tobacco warehouses are cleaned and fumigated, or tobacco is exposed to a freezing temperature for a week or longer or heated to 135 degrees F. Beetles also feed on books, spices, upholstered furniture, and seeds. Use fumigants or contact insecticides but do not contaminate foods.

RED-LEGGED HAM BEETLES feed on cured meats, fish, cheese, and other dried foods. Most damage is done by the larvae, which bore into meat, particularly the fat, and collect around the bones. The adults feed at the surface. A life cycle may be completed in as short a time as 30 days. In the home infested foods should be destroyed. Careful cleaning to eliminate bits of food that might support developing larvae is important. The Larder Beetle (p. 31) is also a pest of cured meats.

TOBACCO MOTHS are closely related to Mediterranean Flour Moth and to the Indian-meal Moth but do not infest grains or flour commonly. They are most damaging to stored tobacco, the caterpillars eating holes through the leaves. They are also common pests of stored chocolate and are sometimes referred to as Chocolate Moths. Nuts and other dried foods may be infested too. Control by methods used for Cigarette Beetle.

CIGARETTE BEETLE

0.1 in.

grub
0.1 in.

RED-LEGGED HAM BEETLE
0.3 in.

larva
0.4 in.

TOBACCO MOTH

0.5 in.

larva
0.4 in.

CHEESE MITE
0.03 in.

CHEESE MITES and closely related species feed on cheese, cereals, flour, cured meats, and other foods, giving them a sweetish odor. Infested flour appears to seethe, though the mites themselves are nearly microscopic. The shed skins, dead bodies, and excrement form a brownish powder. "Grocer's itch" is a skin irritation produced from handling mite-infested flour. Mites do not thrive in dry conditions; hence do not permit stored food to get damp.

CHEESE SKIPPERS are so named because they sometimes flip into the air to move from one spot to another. To do this the maggot curves its body and holds its tail with the hooks around its mouth, then suddenly releases its hold. Normally the maggots crawl in a wormlike manner. Cheese Skippers infest cured meats as commonly as they do cheeses. When full grown the larvae leave the food and pupate in dark crevices nearby. Adult flies are attracted to the odor of cheese or meat, on which they feed and lay their clusters of eggs. A life cycle requires about 2½ weeks. Infested portions of meat or cheese should be cut off and burned. A fine-mesh screen or cloth over storeroom windows and vents will keep out the adult flies. Where infestations have occurred, fumigation may be necessary. In commercial storage of meats, all stages of the Cheese Skipper can be killed by heating meats to 125 degrees F. for an hour or by storage of meats and cheeses at 43 F. or lower.

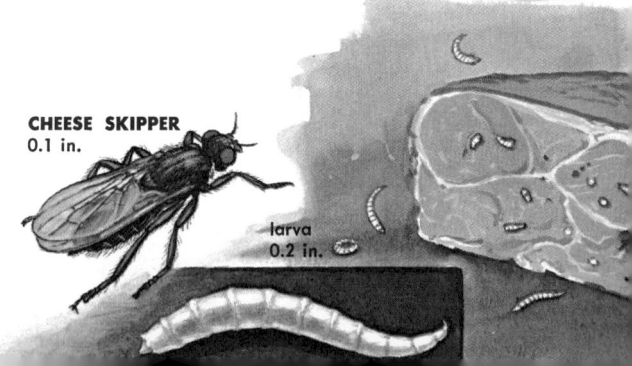

CHEESE SKIPPER
0.1 in.

larva
0.2 in.

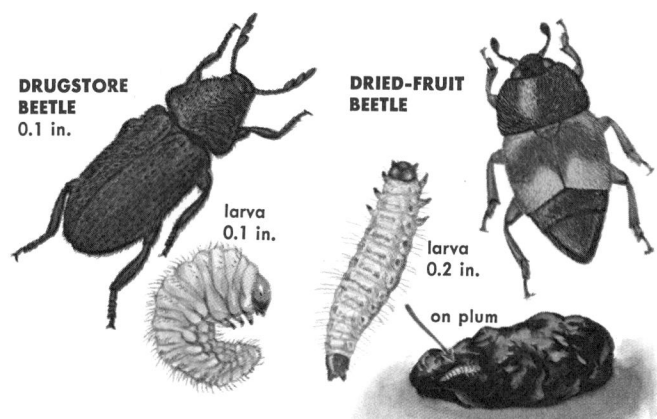

DRUGSTORE BEETLE
0.1 in.

larva
0.1 in.

DRIED-FRUIT BEETLE

larva
0.2 in.

on plum

DRUGSTORE BEETLES are common house and storage-area pests. They eat an amazing variety of substances—bread, spices, drugs (including strychnine), and books. They even bore into lead or tinfoil. In cool climates there is one generation per year; in warm climates, four. Burn infested material or expose to about 150 degrees F. for several hours. Fumigation may be necessary in warerooms.

SPIDER BEETLES feed on dried foods and on feathers, hides, books, drugs, and spices. Unusually resistant to cold, they are active at temperatures as low as 40 degrees F. and are common pests in Canada and northern United States. Many species cannot survive above 80 degrees F. Some, such as the Golden Spider Beetle, are wingless and are spread only by crawling or by man. Clean the infested area and spray with a residual contact insecticide if there is no danger of food contamination.

DRIED-FRUIT BEETLES infest both fresh and dried fruits. They are especially serious pests of dates and figs in California, transmitting the spores of fungi and bacteria that cause the fruit to sour. Female beetles lay their eggs on ripe fruit, in which the larvae feed and develop. A life cycle is completed in three weeks in warm weather. Destroy fruit dropped from trees as it will serve as a breeding area.

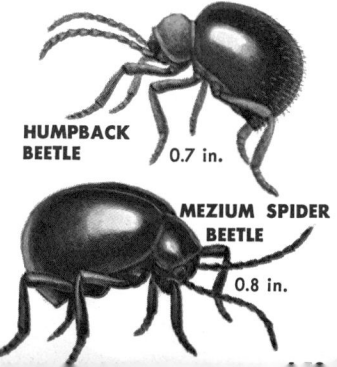

HUMPBACK BEETLE 0.7 in.

MEZIUM SPIDER BEETLE
0.8 in.

4 Melanoplus differentialis
8 Lepisma saccharina
9 Chinch: Blissus leucopterus
Japanese: Popillia japonica
11 Fly: Winthemia quadripustulata
Armyworm: Pseudaletia unipuncta
Braconid: Aphidius testaceipes
Cotton Aphid: Aphis gossypii
Cabbage: Hylemya brassicae
Rove: Aleochara bimaculata
12 Vedalia: Rodolia cardinalis
Cottony: Icerya purchasi
13 Braconid: Apanteles glomeratus
Tobacco: Protoparce sexta
Jap. Beetle: Popillia japonica
Imported: Pieris rapae
15 Tobacco: Protoparce sexta
Tarnished: Lygus lineolaris
21 Rose Scale: Aulacaspis rosae
24 Odorous: Tapinoma sessile
Argentine: Iridomyrmex humilis
Thief: Solenopsis molesta
Pharaoh: Monomorium pharaonis
25 Crazy: Paratrechina longicornis
Cornfield: Lasius alienus
Fire: Solenopsis xyloni
Black: Camponotus pennsylvanicus
27 E. Sub: Reticulitermes flavipes
W. Drywood: Kalotermes minor
28 Blattella germanica
29 Oriental: Blatta orientalis
Brown: Supella supellectilium
Amer: Periplaneta americana
31 Webbing: Tineola bisselliella
Casemaking: Tinea pellionella
Plaster: Tineola walsinghami
Larder: Dermestes lardarius
Carpet: Anthrenus scrophulariae
Hide: Dermestes maculatus
32 Musca domestica
33 Little: Fannia canicularis
Green: Phaenicia sp.
Blue: Calliphora vomitoria
Cluster: Pollenia rudis
Moth: Psychoda alternata
Fruit: Drosophila melanogaster
Eye: Hippelates collusor
34 Silverfish: Lepisma saccharina
Firebrat: Thermobia domestica
Earwig: Forficula auricularia
Cricket: Acheta domesticus
35 Lyctus: Lyctus planicollis
Furniture: Anobium punctatum
Book: Liposcelis divinatorius
Box: Leptocoris trivittatus
Crane: Tipula abdominalis
Springtail: Sira buski

36 House: Scutigera coleoptrata
Millipede: Parajulus impressus
Sowbug: Porcellio laevis
Pillbug: Armadillidium vulgare
Scorpion: Centruroides gertschi
37 Daddylonglegs: Liobunum vittatum
House: Achaearanea tepidariorum
Jumping: Phidippus audax
Widow: Latrodectus mactans
38 Horse: Tabanus atratus
Deer: Chrysops vittatus
39 Black Fly: Simulium venustum
Sand: Culicoides canithorax
Stable: Stomoxys calcitrans
41 Mal: Anopheles quadrimaculatus
Yellow-fever: Aedes aegypti
Salt-marsh: A. sollicitans
House: Culex pipiens
42 Bed Bug: Cimex lectularius
Swallow: Oeciacus vicarius
Swift: Cimexopsis nyctalis
43 Head: Pediculus h. capitis
Body: P. humanus
Crab: Phthirus pubis
44 Hunter: Reduvius personatus
Conenose: Triatoma sanguisuga
45 Itch: Sarcoptes scabiei
Chig: Eutrombicula alfreddugesi
46 Rky. Mt: Dermacentor andersoni
Star: Amblyomma americanum
Dog: Rhipicephalus sanguineus
47 Puss: Megalopyge opercularis
Hag: Phobetron pithecium
Saddleback: Sibine stimulea
Bald-faced: Vespula maculata
Paper-nest: Polistes spp.
Mud: Sceliphron cementarius
48 Dermacentor variabilis
49 Cattle: Boophilus annulatus
Ear: Otobius megnini
Fowl: Argas persicus
50 Cat: Ctenocephalides felis
Human: Pulex irritans
Rat: Xenopsylla cheopis
51 Stick: Echidnophaga gallinacea
Chigoe: Tunga penetrans
52 Head: Cuclotogaster heterographus
Body: Menacanthus stramineus
53 Sheep: Bovicola ovis
Horse: B. equi
Hog: Haematopinus suis
Cattle: H. eurysternus
54 Scab: Psoroptes equi
Itch: Sarcoptes scabiei
Ear Mange: Otodectes cynotis

55 Chicken: *Dermanyssus gallinae*
Scaly: *Knemidokoptes mutans*
Depluming: *K. gallinae*
Hog: *Demodex phylloides*
56 Striped: *Tabanus lineola*
Face: *Musca autumnalis*
57 Horse: *Gasterophilus intestinalis*
Nose Bot: *G. haemorrhoidalis*
Sheep Ked: *Oestrus ovis*
58 *Hypoderma lineatum*
59 N. Cattle: *Hypoderma bovis*
Horn: *Haematobia irritans*
60 Screw: *Callitroga hominivorax*
Sheep Ked: *Melophagus ovinus*
Black Blow: *Phormia regina*
61 *Gryllotalpa hexadactyla*
62 Potato Flea: *Epitrix cucumeris*
Eggplant: *E. fuscula*
Sweet: *Chaetocnema confinis*
Striped: *Phyllotreta striolata*
Pale: *Systena blanda*
Strawberry: *Altica ignita*
Spinach: *Disonycha xanthomelas*
63 Gulf: *Conoderus amplicollis*
Pacific: *Limonius canus*
E. Field: *L. agonus*
64 Variegated: *Peridroma saucia*
Black: *Agrotis ipsilon*
Spotted: *Amathes c-nigrum*
Pale: *Agrotis orthogonia*
65 May: *Phyllophaga rugosa*
Asiatic: *Autoserica castanea*
67 Pea: *Acyrthosiphon pisum*
Bean: *Aphis fabae*
Cabbage: *Brevicoryne brassicae*
Melon: *Aphis gossypii*
68 *Circulifer tenellus*
69 Potato: *Empoasca fabae*
Six: *Macrosteles fascifrons*
S. Garden: *Empoasca solana*
70 Harl: *Murgantia histrionica*
Green: *Acrosternum hilare*
Southern: *Nezara viridula*
71 Tarnished: *Lygus lineolaris*
Squash: *Anasa tristis*
72 Eggplant: *Gargaphia solani*
Onion: *Thrips tabaci*
73 Argus: *Chelymorpha cassidea*
Jamaica: *Eurypepla jamaicensis*
75 Col: *Leptinotarsa decemlineata*
Striped: *Epicauta vittata*
Gray: *E. cinerea*
Spotted: *E. maculata*
Margined: *E. pestifera*
76 Bean: *Cerotoma trifurcata*
Mex: *Epilachna varivestis*
77 Spotted: *Diabrotica undecimpunctata howardi*
Striped: *Acalymma vittata*
78 Vegetable: *Listroderes costirostris obliquus*
Pepper: *Anthonomus eugenii*

78 (cont.)
Sweetpotato: *Cylas formicarius elegantulus*
79 White: *Graphognathus leucoloma*
Car: *Listronotus oregonensis*
Straw.: *Brachyrhinus ovatus*
80 Cabbageworm: *Pieris rapae*
Cab. Looper: *Trichoplusia ni*
Moth: *Plutella maculipennis*
81 Squash: *Melittia cucurbitae*
Pickle: *Diaphania nitidalis*
Melonworm: *D. hyalinata*
82 Potato: *Gnorimoschema operculella*
Beet: *Loxostege sticticalis*
Garden: *L. similalis*
Toma: *Protoparce quinquemaculata*
83 Celery Leaf: *Udea rubigalis*
Celeryworm: *Papilio polyxenes asterius*
Banded Woolly: *Isia isabella*
84 Cabbage: *Hylemya brassicae*
Carrot: *Psila rosae*
Spinach: *Pegomya hyoscyami*
Onion: *Hylemya antiqua*
85 Tomato: *Vasates lycopersici*
Spider: *Tetranychus telarius*
Brown Garden: *Helix aspersa*
Spotted: *Limax maximus*
87 Long: *Pseudococcus adonidum*
Mexican: *Phenacoccus gossypii*
Fern: *Pinnaspis aspidistrae*
Cactus: *Diaspis echinocacti*
Hemi: *Saissetia hemisphaerica*
Brown Soft: *Coccus hesperidum*
Greenhouse: *Orthezia insignis*
88 Greenhouse: *Trialeurodes vaporariorum*
Corn: *Anuraphis maidiradicis*
Chrys: *Macrosiphoniella sanborni*
89 Banded: *Hercinothrips femoralis*
Greenhouse: *Heliothrips haemorrhoidalis*
Glad: *Taeniothrips simplex*
Buff: *Stictocephala bubalus*
90 Chrys: *Corythucha marmorata*
Azalea: *Stephanitis pyrioides*
Cyc: *Steneotarsonemus pallidus*
Bulb: *Rhizoglyphus echinopus*
91 Lesser: *Eumerus tuberculatus*
Narcissus: *Lampetia equestris*
Chrys: *Diarthronomyia chrysanthemi*
Rose: *Dasyneura rhodophaga*
92 Azalea: *Gracilaria azaleella*
Arbor: *Argyresthia thuiella*
Colum: *Phytomyza minuscula*
Larkspur: *P. delphiniae*
93 Colum: *Papaipema purpurifascia*
Lilac: *Podosesia syringae*

93 (cont.)
Oblique: *Archips rosaceanus*
Red: *Argyrotaenia velutinana*
94 Texas: *Atta texana*
Leaf: *Megachile latimanus*
Morn: *Loxostege obliteralis*
Bag: *Thyridopteryx ephemeraeformis*
95 Violet: *Ametastegia pallipes*
Bristly: *Cladius isomerus*
Rose: *Endelomyia aethiops*
Curled: *Allantus cinctus*
96 Black: *Epicauta pennsylvanica*
Rose: *Nodonota puncticollis*
Rose Chafer: *Macrodactylus subspinosus*
97 Fuller: *Pantomorus godmani*
Black: *Brachyrhinus sulcatus*
Rose: *Rhynchites bicolor*
99 Two: *Melanoplus bivittatus*
Differ: *M. differentialis*
Clear-wing: *Camnula pellucida*
Migra: *M. sanguinipes*
Red-legged: *M. femurrubrum*
100 Para: *Lysiphlebus testaceipes*
Greenbug: *Toxoptera graminum*
Aphid: *Anuraphis maidiradicis*
Cornfield: *Lasius alienus*
101 Mead: *Philaenus leucophthalmus*
Legume: *Lygus hesperus*
102 Chinch: *Blissus leucopterus*
Cereal: *Oulema melanopa*
103 Southern Corn: *Diabrotica undecimpunctata howardi*
N. Corn: *D. longicornis*
Grape: *Maecolaspis flavida*
104 Corn: *Chaetocnema pulicaria*
Toothed: *C. denticulata*
Oriental: *Anomala orientalis*
Wheat: *Agriotes mancus*
Plains: *Eleodes opaca*
105 Alfalfa: *Hypera postica*
Maize: *Sphenophorus maidis*
Bluegrass: *S. parvulus*
Curlewbug: *Calendra callosa*
106 Clover Leaf: *Hypera punctata*
Sweet: *Sitona cylindricollis*
Clover Root: *S. hispidula*
107 Lesser: *Hypera nigrirostris*
Boll: *Anthonomus grandis*
108 Cotton: *Alabama argillacea*
Pink: *Pectinophora gossypiella*
109 *Heliothis zea*
110 Army: *Pseudaletia unipuncta*
Fall: *Laphygma frugiperda*
112 *Pyrausta nubilalis*
113 Tobacco: *Protoparce sexta*
114 Stalk: *Papaipema nebris*
S. Corn: *Diatraea crambidoides*
Lesser: *Elasmopalpus lignosellus*

115 Corn: *Crambus caliginosellus*
Alfalfa: *Colias eurytheme*
Clov: *Grapholitha interstinctana*
116 Clover: *Dasyneura leguminicola*
Wheat: *Meromyza americana*
117 *Phytophaga destructor*
118 Wheat Stem: *Cephus cinctus*
W. Joint: *Harmolita tritici*
119 Wheat: *Harmolita grandis*
Clover: *Bruchophagus gibbus*
Thief: *Solenopsis molesta*
120 *Carpocapsa pomonella*
121 Fall: *Alsophila pometaria*
Spring: *Paleacrita vernata*
Eye: *Spilonota ocellana*
122 Peach: *Sanninoidea exitiosa*
Lesser: *Synanthedon pictipes*
123 Peach: *Anarsia lineatella*
Oriental: *Grapholitha molesta*
124 Green: *Lithophane antennata*
Cherry: *Grapholitha packardi*
Fruit: *Archips argyrospilus*
125 *Conotrachelus nenuphar*
126 Apple: *Tachypterellus quadrigibbus*
Flea: *Rhynchaenus pallicornis*
Imbric: *Epicaerus imbricatus*
127 Roundheaded: *Saperda candida*
Flat: *Chrysobothris femorata*
128 Shot: *Scolytus rugulosus*
Peach: *Phloeotribus liminaris*
129 Sinuate: *Agrilus sinuatus*
Japanese: *Popillia japonica*
130 Cherry: *Rhagoletis cingulata*
Apple: *R. pomonella*
Med. Fruit: *Ceratitis capitata*
131 Imported: *Nematus ribesii*
Pear-slug: *Caliroa cerasi*
Woolly: *Eriosoma lanigerum*
132 Apple Aphid: *Aphis pomi*
Spirea: *A. spiraecola*
Rosy: *Anuraphis rosea*
133 Purple: *Lepidosaphes beckii*
Calif: *Aonidiella aurantii*
134 San Jose: *Aspidiotus perniciosus*
Black: *Saissetia oleae*
135 Cottony: *Icerya purchasi*
Vedalia: *Rodolia cardinalis*
Citrus: *Pseudococcus citri*
Citrophilus: *P. gahani*
136 *Dialeurodes citri*
137 Snowy: *Oecanthus niveus*
Citrus: *Scirtothrips citri*
138 Citrus Red: *Panonychus citri*
Citrus Bud: *Aceria sheldoni*
Rust: *Phyllocoptruta oleivora*
139 Eur: *Scolytus multistriatus*
Elm Leaf: *Galerucella luteola*
140 Bronze: *Agrilus anxius*
Poplar: *Saperda calcarata*
Locust: *Megacyllene robiniae*
141 Engel: *Dendroctonus engelmanni*

INDEX

G